Forest of Feelings

JO BROWNING WROE
& CAROL HOLLIDAY

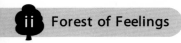
Acknowledgements

We should both like to thank the staff and children at St Matthew's School in Cambridge for entering the Forest of Feelings when it was still uncharted territory.

From Jo: Thank you, John, for such a ludicrous amount of encouragement. Thank you, Alice and Ruby, for listening to my stories with unreserved enthusiasm and tenderness. Thank you, Mum and Dad, for being wise and good parents.

From Carol: My thanks go to my tutors at the Institute for Arts in Therapy and Education – particularly Margot Sunderland and Maggie Wightwyck, for their creative teaching in the realm of feelings. Also to my clients, students and supervisees, from whom I continue to learn. Finally, I should like to thank Steve for his generous support and encouragement and Katy, Rebecca and Billy for their delightful enthusiasm and ideas.

Permission to photocopy

Forest of Feelings
MT00799
ISBN-13: 978 1 85503 387 0
© Jo Browning Wroe and Carol Holliday
Cover illustration © Neil Chapman
Inside illustrations © Neil Chapman and Rebecca Barnes
All rights reserved
First published 2004
Reprinted 2004, 2005, 2007

Printed in the UK for LDA
Abbeygate House, East Road, Cambridge, CB1 1DB, UK

Introduction

This book is about emotional well-being. An emotionally healthy child will be more able to learn, be more sociable, have more satisfying relationships and generally will do better in school and in life than one who is not. The aim of this book is to help you, the busy classroom teacher, support the emotional development of your children – no small task when you have thirty or more of them!

The main part of this book is a story with accompanying teacher's notes and activities. The story is intended for the children's enjoyment in its own right. In the story we meet Ben and join him in his adventures in the Forest of Feelings. Five of the chapters find Ben dealing with a particular emotion: anger, sadness, fear, jealousy and happiness.

The tribes we meet are intended to be ridiculous, because they are stuck in an extreme of one emotional response. At the same time they have some wisdom to pass on to Ben; for example, Volka is absurdly aggressive, but is shocked that Ben hits his sister Anna rather than let steam out of his nostrils as Fumers do. Ben also has something to offer the tribes, both as he reflects on how he responds to his feelings at home and in his human capacity to experience a rich and colourful spectrum of feelings.

Each chapter has creative activities and a circle meeting designed to educate the children about the relevant emotion and about dealing with it appropriately. There are also teacher's notes preceding each chapter to help you work with each feeling.

Before we meet Ben we shall explore some key ideas that underpin the thinking behind this book.

WHAT IS EMOTIONAL WELL-BEING?

An emotionally healthy individual has a wide emotional range. They are able to bear intensity of feeling and to move appropriately between feelings. So, they can feel angry when appropriate – for example when experiencing injustice – and sad when experiencing a loss, and are able to express and think about the feeling effectively.

The emotionally healthy person will be self-aware and have awareness of the feelings of others. In the world of education this is sometimes called 'emotional literacy' or 'resilience'. In the business world it is termed 'emotional intelligence' or 'emotional quotient' and a saying going around at the moment is 'Your IQ gets you your job but your EQ gets you your promotion.'

We want to emphasise that there are not good feelings and bad feelings; there are just feelings, all of which are valid and some of which are more difficult and uncomfortable than others.

There is usually a valuable piece of information to be learned from the feeling: anger might be telling us that our boundaries have been violated or that we are suffering injustice, envy might be telling us what we desire or need. The help children need when experiencing these feelings is the attention of an empathic adult and we shall examine what this means in greater depth later in this introduction.

EMOTIONAL ILL-HEALTH AND ITS CONSEQUENCES

Emotional well-being is a precursor to educational ability. Children who are anxious, angry or grief stricken are not able to learn to their full potential. There is a growing consensus that the underlying cause of many personality and behavioural disorders is the inability to 'digest' painful and unpleasant feelings. When these feelings are left undigested or unprocessed, they leak out in difficult and challenging behaviours such as aggression, bullying, withdrawal, isolation, hyperactivity and separation anxiety, and even in learning difficulties. By educating your children about their emotions you will not only help them, but benefit the whole class environment too. Children struggling with their feelings may exhibit symptoms at home such as sleeping and eating disturbances, soiling or bed-wetting, phobias, obsessions and nightmares. These troubled children, and indeed all children, need help to process their feelings. To process a feeling it needs to be experienced, expressed and thought about in the presence of a safe adult. The role you as a teacher can play in this will be explored later in this introduction.

Babies learn to process their feelings in relationship with their primary carer, usually their mother. The maturation of the developing human brain is experience dependent: the brain is sculpted by this primary relationship. In the beginning when babies cry, their mothers pick them up and cuddle them. The baby is soothed, and in this interaction patterns of experience are laid down in the baby's brain. It is the sensitivity of this relationship that provides the impetus to cope with feelings. A child who is misbehaving may not have developed the mental apparatus to cope with their difficult feelings. At this point we want to stress that such difficulties are not necessarily the parents' fault. The majority of parents do their best. When this falls short of being good enough it is because they do not know how to, or are unable to, do otherwise. Extremely few parents are deliberately cruel to their children.

However, when a child's emotional development is impaired by early experiences, all is not lost. There are optimum times for particular stages of emotional development but the human brain remains plastic throughout life. In

"Teachers as well as parents sculpt brains."

relationship with an empathic adult an older child can learn to deal successfully with their feelings. This means that teachers have an important part to play in the emotional development of the children in their classes. Teachers as well as parents sculpt brains.

THE TEACHER/CHILD RELATIONSHIP

The quality of the relationship a teacher develops with each child in their class is of paramount importance. To build that relationship the teacher needs to model how to handle emotions. It is essential to talk about our feelings because that is how children will learn to reflect on them in their own lives. It is vital to be aware, though, that children will internalise *who* and *how* we are, not what we say. We can talk about expressing and coping with sadness, for example, but if we do not embody and be what we teach, the children will not learn to deal with the experience of sadness themselves. If you are feeling sad, it is acceptable to say to the children, 'I'm feeling sad today.' This communicates to them that it is part of life to have feelings and to talk about them.

To have emotionally intelligent children we need to have emotionally intelligent teachers. We are not saying you have to be perfect. We are saying you need to be human. There are a number of ways to expand your own emotional intelligence. One is to read about emotions and how to understand them – a bibliography is included on page 86 to help you on your journey.

Another way is to take a counselling skills course. You could request counselling skills training for INSET. You may choose to embark on a course of therapy or counselling for yourself; self-awareness is directly linked to the ability to empathise and empathy is a key process in helping children with their feelings.

We have established that the teacher/child relationship is of fundamental importance, and in the next section we shall explore what that might be like. In a relationship that helps a child to digest feelings, the adult will exhibit empathy, acceptance and genuineness.

Empathy

Empathy is about getting a sense of the child's emotional experience, tuning in to how the child is feeling, understanding their reality, stepping into their shoes.

It is about understanding someone from their point of view, by sensing and experiencing their feelings and perspective whilst maintaining a separate sense of self. This maintenance of a separate self is important; without it both you and the child could become lost in overwhelming feelings, and that would not help. What *does* help is being able to bear the feeling, to think about it and to communicate your understanding to the child.

Imagine a child is describing painful emotions in terms of feeling as if they are in a pit. Empathy would be getting as close as possible to the edge of the pit and feeling what it is like to be down there. Not remaining separate would be like getting into the pit with the child. Then you would both be in trouble. The second option is sympathy – we often use the word to mean sharing a feeling and tend to confuse it with empathy. Sympathy involves a sense of merging. Walking away from the pit, not caring, would be apathy – without feeling.

Empathy is the key to emotional literacy and it is an elusive concept. This is probably because very little emotion is delivered or received through words. Most of it is communicated non-verbally through body

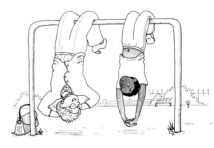

"You're right. It does look different from down here."

language or tone of voice. Empathy is a right brain to right brain transaction. The right side of our brain is largely concerned with feelings and images and the left side with words and reason. This relates to the earlier point about children internalising *who* we are, not what we say.

The ability to read people's emotions from non-verbal clues has been linked to those who are better adjusted emotionally, more popular, more outgoing and more sensitive. In addition, children who show an aptitude for reading non-verbal clues are more popular, more emotionally stable and do better academically, irrespective of their IQ (Goleman 1996).

Acceptance

This describes the attitude of the adult towards the child. Acceptance is valuing the child. It is non-judgemental. The adult prizes the humanity of the child even if the child is displaying difficult behaviour. This attitude is characterised by consistent acceptance and by warmth. Acceptance is also called unconditional positive regard. It is not always easy.

Genuineness

This is a state of being in which your outward responses to the child match your inner feelings and sensations in relation to the child. It is about being authentic and having integrity, about being human and available and responsive. It is also known as congruence.

If a child is being disruptive it is generally better to express your annoyance (if that is what you genuinely feel) – using the formula we offer on page 11 – alongside maintaining an attitude of acceptance towards the child, than to pretend you have no feeling. We are not suggesting that you articulate every feeling that you experience in your working day, but that generally you demonstrate 'what you see is what you get'.

It is possible that a particular child will often arouse difficult feelings in you. In this situation your main task is to reflect on what is happening between you and the child. Some troubled children are able to use a receptive adult to communicate their distress by unconsciously putting their unbearable feeling into the adult. The adult's task is to bear the feelings, and to think about and understand them by consciously experiencing and reflecting on their meaning. In

this way the child receives hope that resolving the feeling is possible. We are not saying that all behaviour is acceptable. We are making a distinction between behaviour and the underlying emotion. Certain unacceptable behaviours will have consequences for the child that are in line with your school behaviour policy, but your attitude towards the child needs to be one of continuing acceptance. This complex phenomenon is explored in depth in Salzberger-Wittenberg *et al.* (1999).

Skills to help you develop empathy

- ### Listening skills

Good listening is a vital skill in developing empathy. We have seen how children need adults to help them process their feelings. The unheard child has no access to healing and children won't be heard if we don't know how to listen. It is a constant challenge to listen well to individuals when you have as many as thirty or so others demanding your attention. These guidelines to good listening will help you make the best of every second of individual interaction:

✔ *Find a suitable place in which to talk – a public space which affords some quiet and will protect the teacher as well as the child.*

✔ *Make yourself mentally available to the child by putting your own thoughts and feelings on one side. If you are thinking about your next lesson or about dinner tonight you won't be able to attune to the child.*

✔ *Use plenty of eye contact (without staring).*

✔ *Allow the child space to talk and tell their story without interrupting or contradicting them.*

✔ *Allow silence if the child is using it to reflect and think, but step in if the silence feels uncomfortable.*

✔ *Be aware of the physical space between you. Position yourself close to the child without being invasive.*

✔ *Acknowledge what the child is saying with nods, 'mmm's, 'oh's, 'ah's and 'I see's. The message you need to convey is 'I am here, I am listening, I am with you.' The responses you make need to be attuned to the emotions of the child and to match the child in volume and pitch. Children have a lot of energy in their feelings and you can afford to turn up the volume of your response in comparison* with talking with adults. A muted response will leave a child feeling lonely and not understood.

✔ *Use mirroring. The next time you are talking with a close friend, notice your body language. You will probably find that your body posture is mirroring your friend's. Your heads will be inclined at the same angle, the tonal quality of your voices will be similar and you will be speaking at roughly the same pace. This is what happens when there is rapport between people.*

✔ *Never try to talk the child out of their feelings. This will only make them feel lonely and not understood.*

- **Encouraging things to say**

  ✔ *Tell me more.*

  ✔ *And then?*

  ✔ *Go on.*

  ✔ *Say more.*

  ✔ *Carry on.*

  ✔ *What else?*

These prompts encourage the child to continue with their story and show that you are interested.

- **Useful questions**

  ✔ *'What', 'How', 'When', 'Who' allow freedom to speak and are good openings for questions when working with feelings.*

  ✔ *'Why' questions demand a reason and will take the child away from feeling and into cognition. Avoid them if you are exploring feelings; use them if you want to encourage the child to think.*

  ✔ *Questions seeking clarification.*

  ✔ *How do you feel?*

Avoid too many questions; children can easily feel they are being interrogated.

Communicating empathy

Once you have experienced empathy for what a child is feeling, you need to communicate your empathy to the child. This enables them to feel understood and no longer alone. If you are faced with an angry child who wants to kick

the door or even their friend, acknowledge their anger and show your understanding by saying 'You are so angry you want to kick the door.' That will have the effect of lessening their desire to kick the door, because they have been understood.

✔ *Paraphrasing what the child has said in your own words demonstrates your understanding and communicates empathy.*

✔ *Reflecting back what you are hearing does the same. It also allows the child to correct you if you haven't got it quite right. Examples are 'What I am hearing is . . .' and 'It sounds as if . . .'.*

✔ *Naming the feeling – this is particularly helpful for younger children who cannot name their feelings. 'You are really sad.' can be very affirming for someone little who is swamped by tears.*

✔ *Offering your sense of the feeling might be best if you are unsure of the feeling. It cannot be construed as invasive. Examples are 'My sense is you are feeling very sad.' and 'It seems you are very sad.'*

✔ *Offering your imagery in relation to their feeling can be a good way of communicating empathy: 'To me you feel like a volcano right now; you're full of energy and about to explode.'*

✔ *Offering a shared experience from literature or film. For example, one little boy was feeling very hard done by and that everyone else in his family was favoured over him. A school counsellor said, 'Sometimes it must feel like living with the Dursleys.' That intervention hit the nail on the head for him and he was deeply relieved that he was understood.*

- **Some magic words to help with empathy**

In the example above, it was important to use the word 'sometimes'. It allows the possibility that it doesn't always have to be like this – it leaves space for hope. Using 'right now' can work similarly: for example 'Right now you feel frightened.'

Sometimes when feeling deep empathy with a child and when communicating that empathy to them it is helpful to use 'for you'. It makes a distinction between you and the child and stops you falling into sympathy to say: 'Life feels very scary for you.'

Working therapeutically with the arts

A child's natural language for the expression of feelings is through image, play and story. When given the opportunity children will spontaneously play out their emotional struggles – in enactments, in drawings and paintings, in sound and in stories. Speaking through the metaphor of a story is a safe way of expressing feelings. If a child speaks to you in story it is crucial that you respond in the same metaphor. For example, if a child is talking about a fairy princess and you think this is about a new baby sister, then respond in terms of the fairy princess. To interpret the metaphor risks exposing and shaming the child – and you might be wrong, so the child will feel misunderstood.

In this book we offer creative activities to accompany each chapter. These are valuable in a number of ways:

✔ *The act of creating can cause something to shift in the child's psyche. For example, for a child feeling overwhelmed by chaos, the act of putting paint on paper can be very soothing, offering relief and calm.*

✔ *Making art encourages connections between the right and left hemispheres of the brain, leading to more integration.*

✔ *The act of creating is engaging and soothing in itself.*

✔ *The image can act as a container for the feelings, offering relief for the child.*

✔ *Images can be used to communicate feelings that are non-verbal or pre-verbal. For example, the child who regularly plays out a monster attacking a young animal is powerfully communicating feelings they are unable to speak about.*

✔ *Images create a shared and rich language with which the child can speak about feelings.*

Creative activities in this book

Each chapter of the story is followed by creative activities designed to enable the child to engage experientially with the story and relate it to their personal lives. These can be carried out with individuals, small groups or a whole class. They can be worked with on a number of levels. They can simply be acknowledged or they can be the focus of an in-depth conversation in which you engage with the child's image, as described later.

Several of the chapters have music and dance activities. We experience feelings in our bodies and these kinds of activities enable us to play with what it is like to be angry, jealous, sad, afraid or happy.

Other activities involve making something, such as a puppet, which allows the children to enter into a dialogue to explore feelings. Puppets feel safe to the child because they are at arm's length, both literally and emotionally. It is a good idea to collect the puppets over the weeks. They can be used in the final session.

SKILLS FOR WORKING WITH A CHILD'S IMAGE

We offer these skills for those occasions when you feel that you need to do more. We are not for a moment suggesting that after every creative activity you should work in depth with every child.

Please note that an image here may be a picture, sculpture, puppet, tune, rhythm, movement or gesture.

Making observations

Notice the things that you see or hear in the child's image, the things that are empirical facts that everyone else will see or hear too. For example, 'I notice everyone is wearing red.' or 'You are playing the drums loud and fast.' Avoid using adverbs and adjectives, which are likely to be your projections and therefore reveal more about you than about the child. The kinds of things to notice are colour, number, size, relationship (a stone on top of a baby for example), volume of sound, pace, texture and so on. Making observations is affirming for the child, who will feel seen as well as heard.

"You have used a lot of black in your painting."

Empathic seeing

Imagine yourself to be in the child's image and think about what it would feel like. Do you feel empty or afraid, or happy and safe? There is a good chance that what you imagine is what the child is feeling.

Images worked with like this provide a powerful insight into a child's inner world. When working in this way it is important to reflect on your experience. What matters is repeated images showing major themes for the child rather than a one-off painting which may be a response to something on television last night.

For example, if a child makes several images involving something small being attacked by many ravening beasts you could enquire what the small thing feels like. You might like to offer that if it were you, you would feel frightened. Remember to keep to the metaphor, as described previously.

CONFIDENTIALITY, DISCLOSURES AND REFERRING ON

This is, understandably, an area of concern and can seem to be something of a minefield. As one student put it, 'Why is the word "ethical" always followed by the word "dilemma"?'

A teacher's pastoral role is an area where they may exercise professional judgement. This means that a teacher does not necessarily have to break confidentiality – it may not be in the best interest of the child – but it is important not to offer or promise total confidentiality.

A teacher must comply with school policy. In addition, LEA guidelines on child protection state that teachers should disclose information relevant to the protection of children to the designated child protection co-ordinator in the school or another relevant professional. McLaughlin *et al.* (1996) is an excellent resource for this area.

If a child makes a major disclosure to you that you believe is a child protection issue, your first task is to offer sensitivity, respect and empathy. The ways of working that we have discussed are safe and respectful, and will help the child to be able to speak about their feelings. Ideally you will have already talked about limits to confidentiality. Your next task is to explain clearly to the child what happens next, who will be told and what they will be told.

LOOKING AFTER YOURSELF

A wise woman once said, 'You have to be a warm radiator to warm others.' What she was getting at was that those who work in the helping professions need to attend to their own well-being. If they don't, they will not be able to do their job. It is part of your job to make sure that you are well and happy and that you make provision for treats for yourself on a weekly basis, be it going dancing or sharing a bottle of wine with a friend.

"You have to be a warm radiator to warm others."

You also need to be alert to those times when you are depleted or unwell. It is better for you and the children that you don't work then and that you take appropriate action.

WORKING WITH CIRCLE TIME

This book includes activities for circle time for every chapter of the story. These are designed to be a key learning opportunity for the children to think about and experience feelings and apply them to their personal experience.

Circles have a long history across many cultures as potent symbols of wholeness. When people sit in a circle everyone has equal status – like the Knights of the Round Table. Our word 'palaver' comes from the African word for a conference where everyone would sit round in a circle and talk until everything had been said. Thanks to the work of Jenny Mosley and others, circle time is an established way of working in many schools (see Mosley 1993). The activities will also work well in the format of classroom discussion.

In this book there is a standard structure for circle time. This allows the children to become familiar with the form.

Now you are ready to journey into the Forest of Feelings and meet Ben and the other characters. We hope that you and your class will enjoy exploring the world of emotions, and that what you find out together will enrich you and your class and enhance your unique relationships.

In the opening chapter of the story the children are introduced to Ben, a boy of 10, to Rusalka, a giant sprite, and to the forest, which is heading rapidly towards disaster. The scene is set for the forthcoming quest. Later chapters concentrate on particular emotions, but here we aim to begin to think about emotions generally. Some children do not have the vocabulary with which to talk and think about emotions. The circle time and creative activities are designed to introduce them to the idea of exploring feelings and to expand their emotional vocabulary and range.

CIRCLE MEETING

In the first circle time it should be emphasised that there are no right or wrong answers when it comes to describing your own feelings. When we trialled the material each child in the circle chose the same emotion in Round 4 because they saw that the first child was affirmed in their choice. They assumed that child must be right and they all copied their response. This highlighted the importance of explaining clearly that there are no right or wrong responses.

This first session includes a brainstorm of emotional vocabulary and affords you the opportunity to get a sense of where the children are in terms of their knowledge of feelings words. Subsequent chapters come with a page of feelings words that can be used for classroom discussions.

The first circle time includes playing with facial expressions. Facial expressions are fundamental to emotional literacy. Over 90 per cent of emotional communication is non-verbal, much of it being transmitted by facial expression, body language, tone of voice and so on. The facial expressions for the basic emotions – fear, anger, happiness, sadness, surprise and disgust – are the same for all cultures, all over the planet.

This chapter aims to open up the world of emotions as a subject that can be discussed and that can be fun and interesting. We hope the children go away with the following thoughts:

- *everyone has feelings;*
- *it is OK to have feelings;*
- *there are lots of different feelings and they all have names;*
- *the main feelings are happiness, sadness, anger and fear;*
- *different feelings have different facial expressions;*
- *we can get to know feelings and about feelings;*
- *some feelings are pleasant and some are uncomfortable, but all are important.*

CREATIVE ACTIVITIES

The book offers you a choice of creative activities. You are not expected to plough through them all; you can choose to do just one or several of them. They offer the opportunity for the child to experience the story and to relate that experience to their own. They can be worked with at a number of levels. They can simply be made and acknowledged, or they can be worked with at more depth as described on page viii.

The treasure box and worry bowl could become very precious to some children and you will need to be mindful of this.

In a different world altogether from ours is a forest, and in the middle of the forest stands a vast table of solid gold. On the table lies a beautiful box, carved out of the finest wood by the finest craftsmen. There are patterns and pictures on each side and jewels on its lid. The box was made to keep something very precious very safe. But the box has been broken and the precious thing it protected is no longer there. Someone is standing next to the table looking at the broken box and she is crying. Her name is Rusalka.

If Rusalka had been crying in our world, her tears would have flooded streets and fields, firefighters would have been busy rescuing people trapped upstairs in their homes, and canoes instead of cars would have been carrying passengers needing to get from one place to another.

Rusalka's tears ran down her beautiful face and fell into the little silver bowl she wore around her neck. As they ran down her face, the tears left rainbow streaks on her cheeks so her face shimmered and glinted red, yellow, indigo, green, orange, violet and blue. The huge gossamer wings that flew her from one world to another lay still on her back, quivering slightly as her shoulders shook with her weeping. Birds were worried and flew anxiously around her. Some landed on the tips of her wings, some flew near her face so they could stroke her cheeks with their feathers.

It was very important that Rusalka collected her tears in the silver bowl, so she didn't try to stop crying. She thought about her forest that was dying and the forest creatures that would die along with it, and she cried and cried and cried. Eventually, the bowl was full and then she stopped.

In our world, Rusalka could lift a double-decker bus, or pull up an old oak tree, but she was gentle and careful as she unhooked the bowl from the chain around her neck and set it before her on the golden table, not spilling a drop.

She stared into it and saw the colours start to swirl and twist around each other. They raced faster and faster round the bowl until they merged and the liquid was completely black and completely still. Rusalka waited patiently. Tiny bubbles formed around the edge first, but soon the whole bowl was bubbling and spitting. It spattered the gleaming table with shiny black flecks.

Rusalka didn't take her eyes off the bowl. At last, the surface grew calm and flat. The black faded to grey, then white, and then was perfectly clear. Rusalka leant her face close enough to see her reflection and let her breath blow ripples on the surface.

It had been many years since she had needed to conjure the Wisdom Speaker. She had been a good guardian of her worlds. They had been healthy and happy and her visits to them had been full of laughter. She had chosen keepers for each of her realms and trained them well, so that while she was gone, they could keep everyone safe. The keepers did their jobs with skill and kindness – especially, she had thought, the keepers of the Forest World: Vigil, Volka, Timor and Terpia. That's why she had left them for many years, thinking all was well, not knowing that the forest had been slowly limping towards its death.

The precious thing that had been in the wooden box in the centre of the forest was called the Spectrum. It was the heart of the forest. Four separate pieces of crystal fitted together perfectly to make a beautiful ball of crystal that glowed and hummed, giving life and strength to the forest.

The most important task that Rusalka gave to her forest keepers was to protect and honour the Spectrum. So, they built the box and kept it at the centre of the forest on the golden table. Each keeper took their turn to stand guard over the Spectrum, and each week the forest people came to honour it. They sat silently before its beauty, watching the colours dart out of it into the air and listening to the delightful notes humming off its rounded surface.

The years passed and Rusalka became a distant memory to the people of the forest. The keepers grew tired of standing guard and moaned amongst themselves. 'Why don't we each take a piece and guard that, then we won't have to leave our families and spend a week alone at the golden table?'

'Has anyone, ever, over all the years we have been guarding it, tried to steal it?'

'Not once! If we promise never to be separated from our piece of the Spectrum, Rusalka will be happy.'

And so they agreed. When they lifted the Spectrum from the box they remembered how beautiful it was. When they held it, they remembered how it buzzed and purred in their hands. They started to wonder if this was a good idea after all, but they had started, and none of them liked to admit to the others that they were scared. Dividing it into four pieces was much harder than they thought it would be. They pulled it, they twisted it, they knocked it, they put it in water, they put it in fire, but whatever they did, it wouldn't separate.

Eventually they put it back in the box. Terpia, who was the best climber, took the box to the top of the tallest tree and dropped it. There was a horrible crack. The box lay in pieces, and so did the Spectrum. They each took a piece for themselves and withdrew to the four corners of the forest. Not one of the keepers pointed out how the colours had bled out of the Spectrum onto the forest floor, or that the pieces didn't hum or look beautiful any more. In silence they each took their piece of the Spectrum and left.

Before long, instead of one forest family, there were four tribes who forgot they needed each other. They didn't eat together, their children didn't play with each other and it didn't take many years for them to forget that they had ever been friends. The forest started to die. Nobody noticed at first. Then, as the trees grew weak and the plants rotted in the ground, it was obvious to everyone what was happening. But they were too ashamed to admit it.

Years passed, and eventually Rusalka came back to visit the forest. Even before her enormous feet had landed softly on the forest floor, she knew something was terribly wrong. It stank. It stank of dying leaves and the dead bodies of little animals. It was dark and damp instead of bright and fresh. Trees that Rusalka had planted hundreds of years earlier, trees that had stood majestic and tall, now drooped, their slimy leaves reaching out to her for help. Their enormous trunks sagged and leant over, moaning softly.

Rusalka swooped over the trees, down to the place of the Spectrum in the centre of the forest. When she saw the empty, broken box she cried out loud and the first rainbow tears sprang to her eyes. She flew above the forest shouting for her keepers, but they all hid from her.

Rusalka knew she had no time to lose. She had to get the four pieces of the Spectrum back together. She knew that special magic was needed to save a dying realm. Her powers were limited. She had to get help. So here she was, standing by the golden table, looking into the magic waters of her tears, ready to meet with the Wisdom Speaker.

She trembled as she saw an old, old face looking up at her from the water. It was so old and crinkled you couldn't tell if it was a man or a woman, or even if it was an animal or a human. Rusalka tried to calm herself, then she spoke to the waters. 'Forgive me, Wisdom Speaker. I have neglected my forest and now it is dying. The Spectrum has gone. I fear it has been broken.'

The face looked out at Rusalka and saw that she was indeed sorry and would do anything to put things right. The leathery old lips opened and said, 'You need a human child. A human child who can persuade your keepers to give back their piece of the Spectrum.'

'How do I find one of those? I cannot go into the land of humans.'

'Rusalka,' the face said, 'the walls between our world and the world of humans are thinnest when there is a child who is very happy or very sad. The walls are so thin you can reach through, Rusalka, and touch the child. Go! A human child can save the forest if it is dying, but once it is dead no one can save it. Hurry, time is short!'

The water turned white, then grey, then black. It bubbled and spat, then the colours returned to race round the bowl. Then they were still. Rusalka drank her tears. With the magic back inside her, she flew over the forest, trailing her words behind her: 'I will return. Take courage. I will return with a human child who can save us.'

Then she flew up to the sky, to the edges of her world, to find where the walls were so thin that she could reach in and touch a human child.

Like Rusalka, Ben had spent most of the day crying. He was 10 years old and he sat huddled in the corner of his tree house at the end of his long skinny garden. He wished he could stay in there until he was old enough to leave home. He didn't ever want to go back inside his stupid house, with his stupid parents and his stupid little bedroom that he had to share with Anna, his even stupider little sister.

That morning she had pulled the plug out when he was playing his favourite computer game. She'd lost his score, and it was his highest ever. So then he pulled the head off one of her dolls.

He got into trouble because what he did was deliberate. Anna didn't get into trouble because what she did was an 'accident'. Ben had to stay in his room and miss Saturday morning cartoons.

Things got even worse when he overheard his mum and dad in their room next door to his. They were talking about the garden. They said it had too many trees and thick bushes, which made it dark and overcrowded. Ben didn't care about that, as long as he had his tree house to go to when he wanted to be alone and quiet. 'The tree house might have to go,' he heard his dad saying. 'If we cut the tree down at the bottom of the garden, we'd get much more light in the afternoon.'

Ben had strict orders not to leave his room, but the thought of his tree house being cut down was too much. He ran out onto the landing, down the stairs, out through the back door, down the garden and up the ladder to his tree house, shouting, 'I hate you! I hate you! I hate you!' all the way, until he sat down. Then he started crying.

Of course, Ben had no idea that all his sadness and anger were making the wall between his world and Rusalka's so thin that she could both hear and see him. He would have been very embarrassed if he had known she was watching. Rusalka understood that it was important not to frighten the human child. She didn't want to behave like a kidnapper. He had to *want* to help, or her plan to save the forest just wouldn't work. Besides, she couldn't help but feel sorry for the boy with black hair that lay in tight spiralling curls on his head, and freckles all over his nose. She had an idea.

She flapped her giant wings and sent colours flying through the air from her world into the next. Ben felt the tree house wobble, like it did when it was very windy. But the wobble didn't scare him. There was something far more unusual to hold his attention. When it was sunny, rays of yellow sunshine poured in through the cracks of the tree house. Well, it was like that now, except the rays he saw weren't just yellow, they were orange, and violet, and red, and green and yellow and blue. They shot through the gaps in the wood and formed a perfect little rainbow right over his head! Ben laughed out loud. It was so surprising and beautiful.

Rusalka saw his smile and heard his laugh and she knew she had chosen the right child. She reached through the wall between their worlds and lifted off the side of his tree house as if it were a piece of paper, sending nails and screws and splinters of wood flying into the garden.

Ben was terrified. His lungs filled quickly and he was ready to scream, but before he had the chance he saw the most amazing sight he had ever seen. It was so wonderful, he stopped being afraid. In the gap where the wall of the tree house used to be was the base of a rainbow, much bigger than the one still hovering over his head. It went up high into the sky and then disappeared. The little rainbow dropped down and nudged Ben's shoulder, pushing him onto the big one. It felt soft under his feet, but he somehow knew it was going to hold him. Filled with a sudden longing to know where the rainbow went, he took a quick look behind at his tree house, turned and ran up the curve of the colourful path.

Ben didn't have much time to imagine where he might find himself at the end of the rainbow. Floating high above the world? Sitting on a cloud? Of all the possibilities that whizzed through his mind as he reached the top and ran down the slope towards the bottom, not once did he think he would find himself standing next to an enormous, smiling fairy. 'You came! Thank you! I'm so pleased!'

When she spoke, her breath nearly knocked him over. Ben was confused, but mostly he was delighted that this amazing creature seemed so happy to see him. No one at home looked this pleased when he walked through the door. 'Who are you?' he asked.

'I am Rusalka. And you, human child, do you have a name?'

'I'm Ben.'

'Hello, Ben. I am grateful beyond words to you. I have a lot to tell you. But I don't have much time. Would you fly with me while I tell you what needs to be done?'

Ben thought he was probably dreaming but decided it didn't really matter if he were. It was such a nice dream. 'OK,' he said.

'Splendid!' said Rusalka, gently picking him up and putting him in a silk pocket next to her heart. 'We are going to my forest, and you are going to save it for me!'

One beat of Rusalka's mighty wings carried them a hundred miles. Ben couldn't speak because the wind whipped his breath away, but he could listen to her heart beating like a big bass drum and he could listen to her rich voice as she told him the story of the forest, about the Spectrum and her keepers, about her guilt at leaving them alone for too long, about the Wisdom Speaker and about the need for a human child to collect the pieces of the Spectrum and put them back together.

By the time they had travelled thousands of miles, across Rusalka's worlds, Ben had forgotten the lost score on his computer game, he'd forgotten about his stupid sister, and he'd even forgotten that his parents were talking about taking his tree house down. By the time they had glided over the forest and landed softly at its edge, Ben was ready to be a hero.

Overall aim Exploring emotional vocabulary.

(ROUND 1)

Aim To warm up, make contact, and have fun.

Pass a smile All stand in a circle holding hands. The teacher smiles at the child on their right. When that child sees the smile, they smile at the child on their right and so on. Once the teacher has sent the first smile, they send a second smile round the circle in the opposite direction by smiling at the child on their left.

Next time round two smiles can be sent in the same direction, the second starting when the first smile has passed about six children.

Once children are familiar with this game, the teacher can choose one of them to begin the round.

(ROUND 2)

Aim Ask children to swap places in response to the statements below to mix the children up so that they work with someone they might not usually choose:

- ◆ *Change places everyone who has felt happy today.*
- ◆ *Change places everyone who has felt sad this week.*
- ◆ *Change places everyone who has felt angry today.*
- ◆ *Change places everyone who has felt afraid this week.*

(ROUND 3)

Aim To expand emotional vocabulary so that children have the words to describe how they feel.

Collecting feeling words Ask the children how many feeling words they can think of. Write them up on a big piece of paper.

(ROUND 4)

Aim To engage with the story and explore feelings, demonstrating to children that people have different feelings about the same things, that this is OK – indeed it is a good thing – and that there are no right or wrong answers.

Question What was your favourite part of the story?

Question Can you name some of Ben and Rusalka's feelings in the story?

Ideally, each child should have the opportunity to answer both questions. If the group is too large for this, then each child should have the chance to answer at least one of the questions.

(ROUND 5)

Aim To explore and play with emotional facial expressions.

Wipe a face The children work in pairs. Child A pulls a face showing a particular feeling (e.g. a sad face). Child B mirrors the face. Child B wipes their face by passing their hand over their face and wiping away the expression and choosing another face (e.g. an angry one). Child A mirrors the new face and so on. This is best demonstrated so the children get the hang of it.

After a few minutes ask for a round of the most interesting faces and ask each child to name the feeling that goes with their face.

(ROUND 6)

Aim To move towards closure.

Open forum is a time to hear any further thoughts or last words on feeling words and/or faces that the children may not have expressed yet.

Question Is there anything else anyone would like to say or to ask about feelings words or faces?

(ROUND 7)

Aim To close, repeat the game used in Round 1.

CREATIVE ACTIVITY 1

Painting

You will need paints, paper, brushes, water and aprons.

Invite the children to paint a picture about their favourite part of the story.

As they work on their compositions you can engage different children in a conversation about their painting. Offer your observations in terms of the colours, shapes and details that you see; for example 'I notice all the flowers are red.', 'I see two figures in your picture.'

In this way you will be avoiding making interpretations which could be invasive and more about you than the child, and giving the child the space to elaborate on the facts with their own feelings about their painting.

This activity would be a suitable one to do after every chapter of the story.

CREATIVE ACTIVITY 2

Masks

You will need paper plates or discs of card, elastic, scissors, felt pens or crayons, glue; and collage material such as sequins, beads, wool, fabric, felt, feathers, tissue paper, glitter, pom poms, shells.

The masks are made by attaching a loop of elastic to either side of the paper plate for the child's ears and cutting holes for their eyes. Some of this may need to be done in advance, depending on the age of the children.

The children are invited to think about different feelings and their associated facial expressions and to decorate their mask to show a feeling. They can then wear their masks for a parade around the classroom. Ask the children to think of names for their masks.

Again, this activity could be one that you do after every chapter. For the next four chapters the masks would be of different tribes the children meet.

CREATIVE ACTIVITY 3

Make a treasure box

You will need a cardboard box for each child and the art materials listed for the previous mask activity.

Invite the children to decorate their treasure box and to make it special. When the box is ready they can fill it with things that mean a lot to them. Some children might want to put in pictures of special people or pets, some might want to write down things to do with people or places or events, some might find objects such as a shell to remind them of a holiday. Some children might put in some school work or other achievement.

Treasure boxes are affirming things to make and can be revisited by the child when in need of comfort. You will need to keep an eye out for any child who has suffered a major loss. This is a particularly beneficial piece of work for such a child and is also likely to evoke strong feelings that will need to be acknowledged and received, using the guidance on page vii.

CREATIVE ACTIVITY 4

Make a silver bowl

You will need : Newclay® (which hardens without firing) and metallic paints.

The children can make simple bowls such as thumb pots or coil pots. These can be painted with the metallic paints when they have dried and hardened.

The painted bowls can be used to contain the children's worries, as Rusalka used her's to collect her tears. The worries can be put on paper in words or in pictures and then placed in the bowl. The bowls need to be kept in a safe place until the worries are dealt with. The act of putting them in another container rather than being kept in the child can offer a great deal of relief to a troubled child.

You will need to give the children the opportunity to share their worries with you in a safe (sometimes this means private) way. Perhaps you could make yourself available once a week for those who need to share a worry.

In this chapter, Ben meets the Fumers, who are always angry and who exemplify the words of the ancient Greek philosopher Aristotle, who said:

> *Anyone can become angry – that is easy. But to be angry with the right person, to the right degree, at the right time, for the right purpose, and in the right way – this is not easy.*

> *Aristotle, The Nicomanchean Ethics (cited in Goleman 1996)*

This chapter is about dealing appropriately with anger. Anger has a bad press. Children, parents and teachers may be afraid of anger. We are usually afraid because we have experienced inappropriate expressions of anger that have involved us or other people in being hurt either emotionally or physically. First, we want to make a case for anger and then explore some creative ways of working with it.

Anger is healthy and useful. It usually arises out of physical or emotional pain. It tells us when our boundaries are being violated and warns us that we need to protect ourselves. We feel angry when we experience injustice and it motivates us to make healthy changes. We need anger to protect and empower us.

- *Anger motivated anti-apartheid campaigners in South Africa to effect change.*

- *Anger motivated William Wilberforce to work to abolish slavery.*

- *Anger motivated Rosa Parks to initiate the civil rights movement.*

- *Anger motivated Bob Geldof to organise Live Aid.*

The trouble with anger is that it is often expressed in a blaming or accusatory way that hurts others, causing more anger and more blame and creating an upward spiral leading to aggression and violence. Children (and adults) need to be taught the magic formula for expressing anger cleanly.

When angry, the thing to do is to use the language of responsibility (a concept from Gestalt therapy) to own the anger and express it in a non-blaming way. Making 'I' statements owns the feeling as your own. Making 'You' statements usually blames the other person. It is better to say 'I feel angry when you . . .' than 'You make me feel angry when . . .'

This formula for expressing anger is well known in the therapy world. When introducing it to children it helps to call it a magic formula. That's far more exciting for them than being given rules. Here is the magic formula:

- ***I feel . . . (angry, furious, frustrated)***

- ***when . . . (say what happened)***

- ***because . . . (what happens to me)***

- ***What I would like is . . . (say what you would rather happen)***

For example:

I feel angry when you take my pencils because I am worried you will lose or break them. What I would like is for you to ask me first and give them back to me at the end of the lesson.

When anger isn't expressed cleanly, it is likely to leak out in undesirable behaviours and symptoms. In Transactional Analysis (a type of psychotherapy) collecting unspoken resentments is likened to collecting loyalty points. When you have a worthwhile amount you cash them in, in the form of a breakdown, an illness or a relationship crisis.

The circle time activities for this chapter are designed to illuminate the difference between emotion and behaviour. It is in the nature of emotion to move us to action. Actually, that is what the word means. It is up to us to ensure that the action is an appropriate one. So, stamping or tearing up old newspaper is OK; hitting your friend is not.

Another important point to emphasise here, in the realm of feeling, is that children learn not *what* we tell them but *how* we are. So, if you have a block in the arena of anger, either you will explode inappropriately or you will be unable to express your anger at all. You will not be able to model this way of being to the children, and they will not be able to internalise more emotionally literate ways of dealing with their anger. If you want to improve in this area, refer to page v. If you find it difficult to express anger, an assertiveness course might help. If, on the other hand, you find anger difficult to contain, then an anger management course will be valuable.

To sum this up:

- ◆ *anger is healthy;*

- ◆ *anger is useful;*

- ◆ *there are clean ways to express anger;*

- ◆ *if anger isn't expressed in a clean way it will leak out in other ways;*

- ◆ *there is a difference between emotion and behaviour;*

- ◆ *all emotions are acceptable, all behaviours are not.*

HOW TO BE WITH SOMEONE ELSE'S ANGER

When you are dealing with an angry child it is important to acknowledge the child's feelings. Good listening dissipates anger; the irony is that often when a child is angry, people stop listening. Acknowledging the anger in words and images also tends to defuse it. Saying to Gita, 'I can see that you are so angry that you want to hit Sarah.' can lessen her

desire to do that. Model to the child healthy ways of being with anger; don't join in. If you do, the situation could escalate. After the anger has been expressed and acknowledged you can explore with the child what they need and what options are available.

From this chapter we hope the children will learn about the following:

- ◆ *how to listen and do your best to understand;*

- ◆ *how to offer empathy;*

- ◆ *not to retaliate;*

- ◆ *not to become a victim by being sucked in;*

- ◆ *how to provide calmness and not join in.*

Ben was suddenly alone again. The bright colours that whooshed and whirled around in the air when he was with Rusalka were gone. He was standing on a muddy path. It was gloomy, cold and silent. Great trees drooped their black branches over him on both sides. Their slimy leaves dripped gooey drops that smelled like rotting compost. The ground was spongy and damp and peppered with little flowers that hung their heads towards the ground. Ben could see they must have been blue originally, but their colour was running down their petals and trickling onto the ground. Ben bent down and lifted up one of the flower heads. To his amazement, it pulled itself away from his hand and slumped back towards the ground. 'Don't worry,' said Ben, feeling sorry for the flower, 'I'm going to make things better. I'm going to save the forest.'

The flower didn't move, but a big drop of blue plopped from its petal onto his foot.

He had felt brave in Rusalka's pocket. When she told him he had to find the four keepers of the forest, and get their pieces of the Spectrum back, he thought it sounded easy. He had to get to know them, she had said, so they would hand over their pieces. No problem, Ben had thought. But now, all alone in the rotting dark forest, he wasn't so sure. What if he couldn't find the keepers? What if they didn't like him and wouldn't give him their pieces of the Spectrum? What if he got lost? What if Rusalka never came back and he was left in this foul place for ever?

Ben walked slowly along the path, not really noticing where he was going. His eyes started to sting and his lip started to tremble. He was about to cry.

He didn't think things could get any worse, but they were about to. A sharp cracking noise ripped through the air and Ben realised he had been shot at! He dropped to the ground and lay on the sodden forest floor, his eyes closed, his heart thumping so fast and hard he could hear it in his ears. He could feel stickiness on his stomach in the gap between his T-shirt and his jeans.

Ben lay still, too frightened to move. He opened one eye and saw to his horror that his arms, stretched out in front of him, were covered with blood. Red streams were running down his arms and hands, onto the forest floor.

Then why didn't it hurt? But no! It *couldn't* be his blood, the red lines stretched out way beyond his fingers. It was light! Red light shining in beams, through the branches of the trees.

Even before Ben could feel relieved that he hadn't been shot after all, there was another 'BANG!' and a whizzing sound right above him. He tried to stay as close to the ground as possible, but he twisted his head to look up and see what was making the noise. It was then that Ben noticed the very tops of the trees had no leaves on at all. They were bare.

BANG! There it was again. To his surprise, at the same time as the explosion, a leaf burst off one of the upper branches and broke into tiny pellets of rot and red sparks. Ben waited for what he thought was a very long time until he decided it was safe to get up. He rubbed at the sticky mud on his stomach with his T-shirt, and managed to spread it further. It smelt disgusting.

This wasn't what he had expected. He thought he was going to be a hero, but here he was, a stinking, muddy mess, with no idea what he should do, surrounded by exploding trees! He decided to walk towards the rays of red light simply because he didn't know what else to do. That had to be better than staying on the dark, drab edges of the forest. Leaving the path, he tripped and stumbled over spongy tree roots that looked like monster fingers, clawing along the ground. With every step that he took, the red glow grew redder. He suddenly realised that whenever a leaf exploded something else was happening: there was a shout somewhere ahead of him.

What Ben saw next made him wonder for the second time that day if he was dreaming. He had arrived at a large circle of trees. Red paper lanterns hung on red rope between the trees. Red ribbons spiralled their way down the mouldy tree trunks. Beneath each swinging lantern was a wooden table laid with wooden plates and beakers. In the middle of the circle of trees was a platform, a great big slab of wood balanced on lots of tree stumps. There were several drums on the platform, and Ben guessed it was probably a stage and that there must be some sort of party about to start. Ben was wondering who the party was for when a host of figures ran out from the trees and into the circle.

Ben was afraid. What if they didn't like him, or wanted to hurt him? What if they were killing the forest and they'd kill him too? He hid himself behind a particularly fat tree that groaned when he stepped on its roots.

The people that had dashed into the centre of the circle were smaller than Ben, but they were stocky and strong looking. Their chests were puffed out and they stomped around with their shoulders pushed back. They wore tight black trousers and big red shirts, and on their feet they wore the biggest, heaviest looking black boots Ben had ever seen. But it wasn't their puffed-out chests or their big heavy boots that made Ben's hair stand on end and put goose bumps all over his body. No, two other things did that. First of all, their skin. As far as Ben could tell, from the tops of their heads to the tips of their toes, they were quite, quite red! Each one was like a sunset that turned the air around it pink – they glowed! The second thing he saw, once he had got over the shock of their skin and looked more closely, was that they had enormous nostrils. Big enough to get your whole hand inside, never mind a finger!

All of them were carrying sturdy wooden trays of food and drink and putting them on the tables. One of them was unloading drinks from a tray onto a table. Another bumped into him and made him spill one. The first one puffed out his chest even further and stamped his big boot on the ground. At that moment, sparks flew out of the boot, a shout flew out of his mouth and a leaf rocketed off a nearby tree. It seemed that every time someone lost their temper, a leaf exploded. All around the circle, the little red people were bumping and pushing, spilling and dropping. Each time, they stamped their feet, puffed out their chests, shouted and sent another leaf shooting from a tree. Ben wondered what would happen when all the leaves had gone.

Three more figures ran into the circle, waving big sticks. They clambered onto the stage. They started turning the screws on the drums and tapping the skins, each putting an ear close to their drum and closing their eyes in concentration. In front of the stage, a jug of juice had been knocked out of someone's hands and two chunky little characters were pushing and shoving each other, chests puffed out and big scowls on both their faces. One of them pushed the other onto the stage, where he managed to knock all the drums over. Ben knew there was going to be trouble now. And there was – for him. Three angry drummers stamped their feet and shouted and then three leaves, just a few centimetres from Ben's face, burst off the tree. He shouted and leapt away, making himself completely visible to the crowd of red-faced, big-nosed creatures.

There was silence as Ben brushed the bits of leaf off his face. The creatures all looked at him, as startled by his appearance as Ben was by theirs.

'Hello, I'm Ben,' he said. Then, seeing their shocked red faces, he said something he had never needed to say in his whole life until this moment: 'I'm a human child.'

Just as he said that, another tray carrier came in. Her crimson hair almost touched the floor – you only saw her boots as they poked through when she took a step. Her hair was so thick it was like a set of curtains.

The waiter who had knocked the drums over ran towards her. 'Volka, look!' He pointed at Ben, 'A human child, it's called Den.'

'It's Ben actually.'

The waiter flashed angry eyes at Ben. A stream of steam shot out of each of his nostrils, so hard that Ben felt his hair lift up. 'Does it matter if it's Den or Ben? What matters is that you're a human child! Now, be quiet!'

The creature with the long hair marched towards Ben and slapped him on the back. 'Greetings, human child,' she said in a loud voice. 'We are the Fumers. I am Volka, keeper of the Fumers. Did Rusalka send you?'

'Yes,' said Ben, starting to feel more confident, and that he should get on with his job of saving the forest, 'Please will you give me your piece of the Spectrum so we can put them all together and the forest can be saved?'

Ben couldn't help feeling important when he said this, but his voice sounded thin and weedy compared to the booming Volka's. He was disappointed to see that she didn't reach into her pocket and hand him the piece of the Spectrum, or look at him as if he was important. Volka frowned. A hiss of steam blew from each gaping nostril, warming Ben's face.

'I've been looking after it for hundreds of years, I'm not just going to hand it over like that! We have to get to know each other first.

Besides, we're about to have a party. It's our Fumer anniversary. The Fumers have lived in this part of the forest for two hundred years. It would be very rude of you to interrupt our enjoyment. We haven't had a party for twenty-five years. I can't stand around talking to you as if I had no care in the world. Here!' she shouted at Ben, handing him her tray, which was heavy with orange bottles. 'Pour these into the glasses.'

Rusalka hadn't told him what an unpleasant place this was going to be. He was going to do what he was told. He untwisted the silver top of a bottle and an explosion of pink froth burst out. Ben quickly pointed it in the direction of the glasses on a tray next to him. Some of them broke because the liquid fizzed and popped so much, but he noticed that glasses were breaking all around him as the waiters were pouring, so he carried on.

By now the drummers were drumming, very loud and very fast. Fumers were flooding into the circle. Ben didn't know if they were coming because the drums were playing or because word had got round that he was there. From all directions, he could hear angry whispers: 'Where's the human child?' 'What's it like?' 'Can it speak?'

They crowded round him. Most of them looked shocked and stroked his skin and pinched his tiny nostrils. They stared at him for a few seconds, but then the drum beats seemed to get under their skin and they just had to dance. Well, that's what Ben supposed they were doing, although it looked more like stamping and stomping to him.

A Fumer thrust a glass under Volka's nose. 'Drink!' the Fumer shouted.

Volka snatched it and shouted back, 'About time!' Both of them puffed out their chests and stamped their feet, and steam flew from their nostrils.

Ben could hardly think for all the popping and whizzing of leaves. Tiny burnt scraps of leaf lay over everything.

The waiter thrust a glass into Ben's hand. He smiled, said 'Thank you' as he usually did when someone gave him something, and took a sip. The delicious bubbles ran across his tongue and bubbled down his throat, leaving a gorgeous strawberry taste. 'Oh,' he smiled, 'it's delicious. Please can I have some more?'

The waiter stood speechless, and Ben thought there might be tears in his eyes. What Ben didn't know was that it had been more than 150 years since the waiter had heard the words 'please' and 'thank you'. The Fumer had almost forgotten that such words existed. His chest deflated and he stared into the distance.

Volka grabbed Ben and shouted to him that he should be dancing, not standing around getting on everyone's nerves. She threw a piece of cake at his chest and barked, 'Why don't you eat our food? Don't you like it?'

Ben was getting fed up. 'Volka, stop shouting at me!'

He walked away from the dancers and sat at the edge of the circle. Volka stomped after him and stood in front of him, with her hands on her hips. 'If I don't shout, you won't know how angry I am!'

'Well, I will actually,' said Ben, wiping the sweat from his face, 'because you keep blowing steam at me – out of your nose.'

'Well, lucky you. You haven't steamed *me* once. For all I know, you're not even angry.'

'I'm not, and I can't *steam* you, my nose isn't built to do that.'

Volka reached out and stroked her stocky finger from the top of Ben's nose to the bottom. She gave it a sharp squeeze. 'Ouch!' said Ben.

'Your nose is very small! Shall I see if I can stretch it?' Her hands wandered back to Ben's face. She poked and pulled his nose.

'Volka, get off! We don't need to blow steam out of our noses where I come from. And we don't have big boots just for stamping, and we certainly don't make leaves burst off our trees just because we're cross.'

A whispy trail of smoke drifted out of Volka's left nostril. She wafted it away, looking at Ben closely, and then grabbed his right ear. 'Is this where you steam from? Or here?' She poked her finger into one of his nostrils before Ben had time to stop her.

'No, Volka. I don't let off steam like you do, none of us does where I come from.'

'Well then, how do you stop yourselves from exploding? You have to let the anger out somewhere.' Then a cheeky smile broke across her rosy face. 'Unless,' she walked behind Ben, and he turned as red as a Fumer when he realised she was looking at his bottom!

'No! We don't let it out of there either!' he said, quickly turning round.

Volka circled Ben, her hair dragging on the ground, her hands still on her hips. 'Then tell me, Ben, what happens when you get angry if you don't stamp, or steam, or burst a few leaves to smithereens?'

Ben didn't know what to say. He knew what he *ought* to say. He ought to say that you count to 10 until you're not as angry, or you talk calmly with the other person and tell them how you feel, or you go for a quick walk. But he kept remembering the burning feeling he had when his computer screen went dead and he lost his best score ever. He remembered how he felt when he yanked the head off Anna's favourite doll.

Volka was impatient for an answer. 'Tell me, Ben, what do you do when you are angry?'

Ben's jaw tightened. He looked down. 'Sometimes I break something that belongs to her, or I hit her.'

Volka looked shocked. Her eyebrows shot up high. 'Who is *Her*?'

'My sister!' said Ben. 'She's always spoiling things, getting in my way, ruining my fun!'

Volka frowned, 'Poor Her, I bet she'd prefer you to steam her and blow off a few leaves rather than break her things.'

Ben hated to hear Volka feel sorry for Anna. After all, it was *he* who had been chosen to save the forest, not her. A burning sensation ran down the inside of his nose, and his eyes stung as two streams of smoke flew out of his nostrils into Volka's face. BANG! A nearby leaf burst off a tree. Volka's smile was so big, her face looked like it had been split in two. 'You see, human child, you are not so different from us after all.'

Ben looked down and could see his own enormous nostrils. He nervously touched his hot nose and noticed his hands were the same crimson red as Volka's. Other Fumers had noticed and seemed delighted. For the first time since he had arrived, there were no stamping of feet and exploding leaves. Ben put his hand back up to his face and felt his warm nose shrinking under his hand. He watched his skin turn from deep red to bright pink, and then back to normal. Thank goodness!

Volka's smile vanished and Ben thought that she looked sad instead of cross. She reached up and took him by the elbow, leading him away from the others. 'Tell me, Ben, have the other keepers given you their pieces of the Spectrum?'

'Not yet, Volka. You are the first keeper I have met. But I do know I haven't got much time, so *please*, Volka, give it to me.'

Volka looked round. She stroked the squidgy bark of the huge tree next to her and it moaned. Slowly, she gathered her huge mass of hair into one hand and flung it behind her shoulders. Ben could see now that she was wearing a thick leather belt, and that hanging from a glinting silver hook was what looked like a piece of glass, jagged and sharp, like a bolt of lightning. She unhooked it from her belt, kissed it and handed it over to Ben. She had tears in her eyes. 'Here, human child. Save our forest.'

'Thank you, Volka. Thank you so much.'

Volka nodded, but didn't say anything. Rusalka had given Ben a leather purse with a thong attached to it. She told him this is where he must keep

the pieces of the Spectrum. He carefully put the jagged piece of crystal into the purse, waved goodbye to the Fumers and headed back towards the path. He heard Volka shout, 'And if any of those other keepers gives you any trouble, just tell them they'll have me to deal with!' Ben smiled and was not surprised when an exploded leaf hit him on the back of his neck.

Overall aim To learn about anger and clean ways of expressing it.

ROUND 1

Aim To warm up and have fun.

The storm

All sit in a circle with both feet flat on the ground. The teacher tells the story of a storm and invites the children to join in with the sounds and actions.

Once upon a time there was a forest and the wind rustled through the trees.

This is accompanied by rubbing the palms of the hands together to make a rustling noise.

Then it began to rain.

This is accompanied by gentle finger clicking.

Then it rained a little harder.

Louder finger clicking, moving to hand clapping, slowly becoming faster and louder.

Now it begins to thunder.

Feet stamping as well as loud clapping reaching a crescendo and then beginning to slow and fade.

The storm passes.

The children are taken back through the sounds and actions to the rustling in the forest.

The storm is over.

ROUND 2

Aim To engage with the story and reflect on anger. The questions elicit different ways of showing anger.

Question How do the Fumers let out their anger?

Question How do you let out your anger?

Allow each child the opportunity to answer one or both of the above questions, depending on the size of the group.

ROUND 3

Aim To explore ways of expressing anger and to distinguish between clean ways and messy ways.

Introduce the idea of clean anger and messy anger and give examples. Clean anger is non-blaming and safe. It includes talking, ripping up newspapers and hitting cushions. Messy anger includes blaming people, hitting people and so on.

Have on a flipchart a large piece of paper divided in two down the middle. Ask the children what kind of things people do when they feel angry. Get them to say if the examples are clean or messy, and write the clean examples on one side and the messy ones on the other.

ROUND 4

Aim To introduce the magic formula.

'I am going to tell you a magic formula that helps you let out your anger in a clean way. Here it is.'

Introduce the magic formula on page 11 and discuss it, giving an example. A current example would be ideal as this will be more alive.

ROUND 5

Aim To move towards closure.

Open forum to hear any further thoughts or last words on the Fumers and anger.

Ask if there is anything else anyone would like to say or ask about the Fumers or about anger.

ROUND 6

Aim To close.

Pass a squeeze All stand in a circle holding hands. The teacher squeezes the hand of the child on their right. When that child feels the squeeze, they squeeze the hand of the child on their right and so on. Once the teacher has sent the first squeeze, they send a second squeeze round the circle in the opposite direction by squeezing the hand of the child on their left.

CREATIVE ACTIVITY 1

Drumming and dancing at the Fumer party

This music activity is designed to enable children to explore the emotion of anger freely. It has a necessary element of spontaneity. Depending on how familiar your children are with the thoughtful use of instruments, musical composition and role play, you could do this with smaller groups. These could come together for a larger performance later. You will need drums, robust percussion instruments such as wood blocks and claves, and space to move about in.

This activity can follow a rereading of the passage starting at *Rusalka hadn't told him what an unpleasant place this was going to be* on page 18 and continuing to *His chest deflated and he stared into the distance* on page 19.

Invite the children to explore the instruments and notice what each sounds like. Allow a few minutes for this. Ask them to imagine the sounds the Fumers would make. Help them flesh out their ideas by asking questions about the sounds: loud or quiet, low or high, tinkly or squeaky.

The children are invited to be Fumers at the party and play the Fumers' music. Each child then chooses the instrument they would like to play. The music can be accompanied by dancing. Anger involves lots of energy. It is contained in the body in the legs, pelvis and jaw, so lots of stamping and yelling can be encouraged. Lots of noise is fine.

You might like to have half the group drumming and half dancing, and then swap over. Encourage the children to use all the space available. A good way of doing this is to draw a picture (or lines) on the floor in chalk and get them to dance all over the lines.

To close, conduct the group with arm movements to decrease the volume and stop the music. You could conclude by playing some calming, soothing music.

CREATIVE ACTIVITY 2

Fumer puppet

You will need the template of the Fumer's face on page 82 copied onto card, paints, felt tips and lolly sticks.

Invite the children to cut out the template. They can then decorate the puppet with the art materials provided. The Fumer can be attached to a lolly stick to make a simple puppet. Ask the children for a name for their puppet. Allow them an opportunity to role play with their puppet. This will enable you to observe what takes place. If you choose to make puppets for each subsequent chapter as well, they can be collected and kept for a role play after the final chapter.

CREATIVE ACTIVITY 3

Paint a volcano

You will need paper (preferably a large piece), paints and brushes. Invite the children to paint a volcano. Help them to flesh out their ideas by asking them to imagine that they are a volcano and to think about what kind of volcano they are. Are they big or small? Hot or cold? Erupting or dormant? What colour are they? What texture, hard or soft? You could use non-fiction books as a reference for this activity.

As an extension to this the children can be invited to write down the words that go with being a volcano and to bring the words together to make a poem.

CREATIVE ACTIVITY 4

Anger outlines

You will need sheets of paper large enough for a child to lie on and be drawn round (tape sheets of A2 together if necessary), felt tips, scissors and sticky tape.

Working in pairs, the children draw round each other on their sheets of paper. They can then colour in the places where they feel anger in their bodies when aroused. Some children may want to draw pictures within their outline to indicate what they feel inside when they are angry.

ACTIVITY SHEET

The photocopiable sheet on page 25 is a collection of words relating to anger that can be displayed as a poster and used in classroom discussions about anger.

The tribe of angry feelings

irate

rage

fury

hate

annoyed

irritated

angry

wrath

frustration

hostility

resentment

cross

Sadness is an emotion that brings with it a different physiology from that of anger. Anger is highly arousing and full of energy. Sadness, by contrast, is of low energy, slow, and makes us withdrawn and reflective. When sad we tend to turn inwards into ourselves rather than out into the world. We reflect rather than embarking on new projects.

Sadness often accompanies loss. The reflective stance allows us the time to come to terms with the changes resulting from loss. It gives us the chance to reorient ourselves, to make adjustments, develop new meanings and reach an understanding of the new situation. In the case of bereavement this means a new identity.

When we feel sad we cry. Again this is a very useful response. Crying is a behaviour that elicits care giving. In an effective situation the care giver empathises with the child; this allows the child to process the feelings and the child is comforted. In our story Ben goes to his tree house to cry alone, thus depriving himself of the possibility of being comforted by another and possibly exacerbating his sadness with isolation, loneliness and alienation.

The Sobalots by contrast are constantly crying together and comforting each other, to such an extreme that they only get and give attention to each other's sadness. Alice Miller wrote about how children are programmed to get Mummy's smile and avoid her frown. If sadness is the only feeling that gets you attention, then you will eventually learn to deny other feelings in favour of exhibiting sadness. The thrust of this book is that it is important to affirm all feelings expressed by a child.

CIRCLE MEETING ACTIVITIES

These activities are designed to stimulate thinking and discussion about sadness and ways of expressing it. We have in our culture a gender bias. It is more acceptable for girls to cry than boys.

Children need to know that crying has a purpose and that it can be helpful. They need to know that it is important to be comforted when they are sad and that being with a safe person is the best way of achieving this.

LOOKING OUT FOR VULNERABLE CHILDREN

You will need to pay special attention to any child who has experienced a loss or bereavement. Bearing in mind that any change brings with it loss, moving house could be experienced as a loss by some children, even though it is experienced as exciting by others. The story and activities might bring to the surface strong feelings in some children and these feelings need to be received with empathy and understanding. This might mean special provision being made, such as a quiet place or one-to-one time. A child who has a reputation for being a 'cry baby' might also be vulnerable in these activities and you need to be mindful of them.

We hope that at the end of this chapter the children will have learned that:

- ◆ *sadness is healthy;*

- ◆ *sadness is useful;*

- ◆ *our bodies react in certain ways when we are sad and crying is an important part of that;*

- ◆ *being with someone when you are sad is helpful.*

Ben walked for a long time along the dismal forest path. It felt good to have Volka's piece of the Spectrum safe inside his purse, but he wished he knew where to go next. Then he noticed that the leaves on the trees were covered with blue spots. Polka dot trees! Were the people he was about to meet going  to have polka dot skin? After the red Fumers with their giant nostrils, he thought nothing would surprise him. Ben reached out to touch one of the spotty leaves and noticed his own hand was now covered with blue spots. He touched one and discovered it was a drop of water. At home, you needed lots of water before it looked blue, but here just one drop was the colour of the sea on a sunny day.

It was raining now, steadily but gently, and although it was covering him with blue spots so he looked like he had a strange kind of measles, he didn't feel wet. The drips sat on his clothes like sapphires; they didn't soak in at all. He thought the brightness of the drops was dazzling his sight and that was why everything else looked blue. But then he realised there was a blue glow coming from his right. As he walked towards it, the light grew more intense. Ben could not only hear the splat, splat, splat of the drips, but something else too. Was it crying? A few more steps and Ben found himself at the edge of a clearing. He looked for the biggest, spottiest tree and stood behind it, peering round.

The first thing he noticed was a beautiful waterfall, pouring silently into a lake. It cascaded down between the branches of two huge trees, but when Ben looked up, he saw no cliff or rocks over which the water could be falling. The trees that surrounded the lake looked *very* sick. Ben worried that the forest seemed to be getting worse. These trees couldn't stand up at all. They were bent over double, so that the top branches which should have been reaching high up into the sky were drooping in the lake, oozing black gunge into the blue water.

Behind the curtain of the waterfall, Ben saw a huddle of people in a circle with their arms round each other, heads down. He couldn't see them very clearly through the waterfall, but he could tell they were a similar height to the Fumers. Their shoulders were hunched over, so they looked smaller. They all had long grey hair that flowed down their backs, like their own little waterfalls. Ben was right, it *was* the sound of crying he could hear. They were all sobbing!

After a minute or two, Ben saw through the blur of the waterfall that the circle of people had straightened out into a line. Together they stepped through the

waterfall, stood for a second on the edge of the lake, then dropped noiselessly in. Before their bodies plunged into the water, Ben had time to see that they were all wearing black swimsuits, old-fashioned-looking ones that covered their arms completely and went down to their knobbly knees. They each had a different number pinned onto their front. When their faces bobbed up to the surface, Ben was glad he could have a good stare at them without being seen. He found himself open mouthed with surprise, looking at white and blue striped faces!

Ben was learning that things in the forest were different in many ways to home. When *he* jumped into cold water with his friends, there was always a lot of splashing and shouting, climbing out and jumping back in, clambering onto shoulders and pushing each other under. Not here.

These people floated gently on their backs, trod water or just hung onto the side of the lake and slowly waved their legs out behind them. They didn't thrash or splash or kick. They didn't shout or laugh or joke. They simply wept. Every now and then two or more would float together, or tread water together, patting or stroking each other as they cried.

This tribe was a lot quieter and calmer than the Fumers and there weren't nearly as many of them. Ben knew that sooner or later he had to make himself known. I'm just going to have to step out from behind this tree and introduce myself, he thought. The droopy trees round the lake worried him. He suspected he didn't have long left and he still had three pieces of the Spectrum to collect.

He took a deep breath, but before he moved or spoke, lots of others appeared from the trees on his left. They were dressed in black too, in long robes that reminded Ben of nighties. Just as miserable as the swimmers, they carried wooden folding chairs and placed them neatly around the lake, so that the whole expanse of water was surrounded by a circle of weeping, stripy faces.

From behind the waterfall came a single figure carrying something that glinted in the light. Maybe it was a piece of the Spectrum! Ben leant forward onto the tree to get a better look. The tree let out a loud painful sigh and, to Ben's horror, fell right over. Ben was left sprawled on top of the fallen trunk, with at least fifty unhappy but surprised faces looking at him.

'I'm so sorry!' he said, stroking the tree. In spite of his embarrassment, he hated to think he had pushed the poor thing over.

The figure carrying the glinting object came towards him. Ben could now see that it wasn't a piece of the Spectrum, but a big silver cup like the football trophy his team had won. The little woman carrying it looked old, and close up Ben couldn't tell if the long flowing mass reaching down to her knees was hair or water. It seemed to move and flow, and it definitely dripped – he felt it on his own toes. She wore a long black robe like the rest, with a rubber purse strapped to a belt round her waist.

The old woman carefully put the cup down on the ground. Then she slowly reached up and touched Ben's cheek. 'Why is a dry-faced person coming here? Who are you?'

'My name is Ben. I'm a human child and Rusalka sent me to save the forest.'

The sound of group crying grew louder, though Ben couldn't think why. Surely they were pleased that he had come to help them? He tried not to mind the old woman stroking his face over and over again, and asked, 'Are you the keeper?'

She nodded slowly and Ben felt more of her tears plop onto his own foot. 'I am. My name is Terpia, keeper of the Sobalots.'

But Ben hardly heard Terpia introduce herself. It was his turn to be fascinated by a new face. Up close to a Sobalot, Ben noticed that in fact their faces weren't striped. They were covered with streams of blue tears and their eyes had little holes round them, and from each hole came a steady stream of blue water. 'Goodness,' he said. You do a lot of crying round here, don't you?'

'Sadly, we do,' said Terpia mournfully. 'But then, there's so much to cry about. The lake you see is filled with our tears.'

Ben waited politely while Terpia cried for a few minutes. Then she said, 'Ben, do come and sit down. Our annual diving competition is about to take place. Each year, ten Sobalots are chosen to dive for the silver cup. It is the saddest day of our year.'

'Why is it sad?' asked Ben, confused. At school, sports day was his favourite event of the whole year.

Terpia looked up at Ben, tears dripping from all round her eyes, and her bottom lip wobbling. 'It is sad because nine of them will lose! Nine of them don't get to keep the cup, poor things! Imagine how upsetting that will be for all those families whose loved ones don't win.' Terpia had to stop talking to cry properly.

'But the winner is happy, surely? The winner gets to keep the cup. And the family of the winner must all be happy?' said Ben, giving Terpia the chance to squeeze out her sodden hair into the lake. 'Can't you be happy for them, instead of unhappy for the others?'

'That's a funny way of viewing it,' said Terpia, looking puzzled. 'How unpleasant for all the others. Come, we must start the competition.'

Ben sat on one of the wooden seats at the lake's edge, while Terpia, old as she looked, climbed slowly but gracefully up a tall tree next to the waterfall, holding on tightly to the silver cup. The tree groaned and moaned but seemed just able to hold her weight.

The ten swimmers climbed out of the water and stood on little tree stumps that surrounded the lake. They were obviously used as diving boards. One by one, from her high branch, Terpia called out their names. When each one waved to the crowd, a little group – who Ben guessed must be their family – would cry even more loudly.

Terpia held the cup above her head, her sleeves falling back to reveal white, wrinkled arms. For a moment all the crying stopped and there was complete silence. Then she simply let go of the cup so it was carried down by the flow of the waterfall into the depths of the lake of tears. Terpia made her way back down the tree. Her long hair dripping, she came and sat next to Ben.

The crowd watched in silence as the swimmers dived into the lake with gentle plopping noises.

Piles of ironed white handkerchiefs and little buckets were handed round to the crowd. All eyes were on the surface of the water, which had grown so still it was hard to believe there was anyone under there. Then there was a cry as one Sobalot burst out of the water, gasping for air, and held up their empty hands to the crowd. Four Sobalots to Ben's left wailed and buried their faces in their white handkerchiefs. They then squeezed their hankies into the little buckets. When they were full, they were emptied into the lake.

The empty-handed swimmer climbed out and sat on their tree stump, crying and waving to their family. Seconds later, the surface of the lake was broken by several heads at once, all open mouthed, gasping for air. Still no cup. Then a pair of skinny arms shot through the water's surface with the cup held triumphantly. Instead of the cheer that Ben expected, a wail of dismay filled the air. All except five people in the crowd sobbed into their hankies. The lake was almost overflowing onto the grass – so many buckets of tears were being poured into it.

The family of the winner shook hands with each other and sat back in their chairs, looking slightly ashamed. The winner went to stand on a large tree stump by the waterfall. All the other divers stood sobbing on their diving boards.

Terpia walked over to the winner and said, so quietly and quickly that Ben only just heard, 'I pronounce you the winner and the keeper of the cup for this year. Well done.' There was a very quiet ripple of applause. Then Terpia turned to the others. This time her voice was louder and she spoke very solemnly and slowly. 'And now let us honour and pity those who have not won, who have to go home without the cup, who had their chance and failed. Let us despair alongside those who will only be remembered as losers.'

Ben watched amazed as everyone, including the winner, clapped and cried, cried and clapped. Terpia went from one loser to the next, hugging and stroking them, squelching her way around the soggy circle. Ben couldn't bear it. He strode over to the winner, who was standing with her silent relatives.

'Well done!' he said. 'I could never have held my breath for that long. You must be proud.' The Sobalot looked at Ben, several tears about to drop from her surprised eyes. Ben saw a smile twitch at the corners of her mouth, but immediately she put her hand up to cover it. Ben turned to the miserable family. 'Come on! Congratulate her. Didn't she do well?'

The oldest-looking man from the group shuffled nearer to Ben, 'We're pleased, of course,' he said, looking at the ground, 'but we mustn't make a fuss about our happiness. It wouldn't be fair on the ones who have lost.'

Ben made a beeline for Terpia, who was sitting by the lake. 'This is crazy! You make more of a fuss of the losers than of the winner!'

Terpia dabbed her eyes with her hankie. 'Of course we do, we can't ignore someone's sadness.'

'But you ignore the winner's happiness. She and her family weren't allowed to celebrate. What's the point of having a competition if the winner can't be congratulated properly?'

The holes around Terpia's eyes were red from all her crying. Ben wondered if Terpia cried more than everyone else because she was the keeper. 'Surely you don't have to cry *all* the time?' said Ben. 'There must be some things you can all be happy about together.'

'A good cry is often the best thing, Ben. Let it all out.' Terpia bent close to Ben and stroked his face. 'So dry, so very dry!' Then she leant even closer and looked at Ben's eyes. 'No wonder you don't cry much, you haven't got any weepers!'

'I have,' said Ben. 'I just haven't got as many. Look.'

Ben pulled the skin down just below his eye, so Terpia could see his tear duct. Terpia actually laughed. 'One tiny weeper in each eye! Your lake of tears must be tiny'

'We don't have a lake of tears.'

'No lake of tears?' said Terpia sadly, trickles of blue spilling down her cheeks once more. 'Then where do you keep your tears?'

'We don't. We just wipe them away. Or try not to cry at all, at least not in front of people.'

Terpia's mouth flew open in shock. 'You cry on your own? But why?'

'Because only babies cry in public. I'm 10.'

'But who comforts you?'

'Well, my mum would if I let her, but I prefer to go to my tree house on my own and cry there until I've finished.' His tree house! He'd forgotten about that. It might have been chopped down by now! He might no longer have anywhere to go to cry. That thought made him want to cry. Suddenly, the rims of his eyes stung and he couldn't see at all. It was like opening his eyes under water without goggles. Tears were oozing from all round his eyes.

'That's more like it,' said Terpia, holding her arms out to Ben. Ben surprised himself by leaning his head on Terpia's bony shoulder and letting the sobs shake their way out of him. His tears ran fast down Terpia's back and into her flowing hair. 'Doesn't that feel better?' asked Terpia a few minutes later.

Ben breathed deeply. He did feel as if he had let go of something heavy. 'Yes, in a way. But I wouldn't want to cry like that *all* the time. You can't be miserable for everyone all the time, or life would be no fun.'

'Fun?' said Terpia, with a faraway look in her eyes. 'I think I had fun once, but I've got absolutely no idea where it went. Our tears are all we've got, so we must keep them. That's why we've got the lake.'

They both looked over at the circle of water. Black spirals of mould were winding their way from the rotten branches above and down into the blue water. Terpia looked down at her belt. She unzipped the rubber purse that was attached to it and pulled out what looked like a piece of pale blue glass. It was the shape of a perfect teardrop. 'We cry most about the forest dying, but however much we cry it doesn't stop the decay. Our tears can't help it.' She looked at Ben and stroked his face for a last time. 'Maybe a dry-faced one needs to do that.' She slowly reached out to Ben, holding the glass teardrop. 'Take it back to where it belongs, Ben.'

Ben held the tear in his hand for a minute before putting it carefully in his purse with Volka's lightning fork. Two down, two to go. 'Thank you, Terpia. Please cheer up. I'm halfway there now.'

Terpia gave Ben a last hug, her soggy head soaking into his T-shirt, her weepers dripping down Ben's front.

'Why are you crying *now*, Terpia?'

'What if you don't find them? What if we all die?' she wailed.

'Sometimes, Terpia, we need to look on the bright side. When it's all over, I'm going to tell you a really funny joke. I want to see you laugh!'

Terpia shook her head sadly and waved Ben goodbye.

Overall aim To learn about sadness and to think about what happens in our bodies when we are sad.

ROUND 1

Aim To warm up, make contact and have fun.

Pass a handshake All stand in a circle holding hands. The teacher begins by gently shaking the hand of the child on their right. That child passes the handshake on to the child on their right, and so on. When it returns to the teacher, they reverse the direction, passing it to the left. On the third round two handshakes could be sent, so that when the first handshake reaches the sixth child, a second one is sent chasing after it.

ROUND 2

Aim To engage with the story and think about sadness. The questions explore what it is like to be sad.

Question In the story what do the Sobalots do when they are sad?

Question What did Ben do when he was sad?

Question What happens in your body when you cry?

Allow each child as many opportunities to answer as possible.

ROUND 3

Aim To learn about sadness and to consider that crying might be useful, embarrassing and so on.

Have a large piece of paper on a flipchart and divide it down the middle. Write the first two questions below on either side.

Question What are the OK things about crying?

Answers to this might include such things as 'getting comfort', 'people know and can help', 'feel relieved'. A point to make is that crying by yourself can be very lonely. Being with someone is often much more comforting.

Question What are the difficult things about crying?

The answers are again written in the appropriate column. They may include such things as 'it's embarrassing', 'feel out of control', 'get a runny nose', 'you look funny'.

Question Do you think crying helps? What else might help when you feel sad?

ROUND 4

Aim To move towards closure.

Open forum to hear any further thoughts or last words on sadness.

Ask if there is anything else anyone would like to say or ask about the Sobalots or about sadness.

ROUND 5

Aim To close.

Pass a smile All stand in a circle holding hands. The teacher or a child chosen to start smiles at the child on their right. When that child sees the smile, they smile at the child on their right and so on. Once the first smile has been sent, a second smile is sent round the circle in the opposite direction.

CREATIVE ACTIVITY 1

Working with clay

You will need: Newclay® (which will harden in air without having to be fired in a kiln).

Invite the children to play with the clay, to shape it with their hands and to get the feel of it. Ask them to remember the part of the story that felt most important to them and to make an image of it using the clay.

Your task, in working with the children's images, is to make observations, ask open questions and acknowledge any emerging feelings, as described on page viii.

CREATIVE ACTIVITY 2

Sobalot puppet

Use the template of the Sobalot's face on page 83 to make copies on card. You will also need paints, felt tips and lolly sticks.

Ask the children to cut out the face. They can then colour the Sobalot face. The face can be attached to a lolly stick to make a simple puppet. Tell the children to choose a name for their puppet.

The children could imagine that they are Ben arriving at the lake of tears and meeting the Sobalots. They have an opportunity via the puppet to interview a Sobalot and find out more about them.

CREATIVE ACTIVITY 3

Write a poem

You will need paper and pencils.

Begin by asking the group to brainstorm words and ideas that go with sadness. Ask them what sadness feels like and what happens in their bodies when they feel sad.

Get them to complete the sentence *Sadness is like . . .*

You will then have a collection of associated words. The children can be invited to make them into a poem.

They should work in pairs or small groups and can choose any poetry style. Some could write their poem in the shape of a teardrop, some could write a *haiku* poem.

Haiku is a Japanese style of poetry. *Haiku* poems traditionally have seventeen syllables and comprise three lines. The first line has five syllables, the second seven, and the third five.

Some could write their poems with the first lines beginning with the letters in 'sadness'. Here is an example:

> *Sunshine fades*
> *And all light dims.*
> *Darkness falls*
> *Night has come.*
> *Every laugh has gone,*
> *Smiles have fled,*
> *Solemn silence rules.*

CREATIVE ACTIVITY 4

Water music

This activity is most suitable for small groups of children. You will need a water tray for the children to stand at, and items that can be used to make a sound in water. Examples are straws and tubes for blowing bubbles, pipettes for making drops of water, containers of varying sizes for pouring, different-sized pebbles for plopping, syringes for squirting, water wheels and watering cans.

Invite the children to explore the sounds they can make with the water and the equipment. When they have discovered as many sounds as they can, they can play some music together. After rehearsing they might like to play their composition to the rest of the class.

This activity is likely to result in hilarity. That is fine. Laughter is a good teacher as well as good medicine.

Other members of the class can move to the music, creating a Sobalot dance and enacting crying.

The tribe of sad feelings

sorrow

gloomy

melancholy

grief

lonely

dejection

low

mourning

sad

despair

misery

Fear, like anger, is an arousing emotion: blood is pumped to the muscles, especially those in the legs, leaving the face white. We talk of our blood running cold. The body freezes for a moment, preparing for fight or flight depending on the assessment of the threat. The emotions of fear and anger are closely linked. It is well known in military circles that if an attacking person begins to retreat they begin to feel fear, and if a frightened person turns to attack they become angry and unafraid. This gives us a clue for working with fear – to overcome fear a person needs to take action rather than be passive. Proactivity and taking responsibility are the best antidotes to fear. Working with the arts and play are vital as they are active forms of working through feelings.

Many children's fears are manifested at night when they are alone in the dark. The underlying fear might be a separation anxiety, fear of abandonment, fear of invasion, fear of humiliation, fear of failure – or of rejection, of having no friends or of being shamed. The fear becomes a monster that lives under the bed or behind the curtains. In this chapter we meet the Trembolos, who live in a twilight world of permanent fear where bedtime and scary monster watch are relentless. Monsters are very real to children and meeting them with reason in the form of 'there is no such thing as monsters' is unlikely to be effective. Employing a potent form of 'magic' is more fruitful. These monsters live in the realm of the imagination and it makes sense to meet them in that realm.

One little boy was helped with his night-time fears by putting a magic feather under his pillow to keep the scary monsters at bay. Putting on an invisible cloak that protected her from terrifying dreams helped another child.

Other fears are in the realm of physical reality. Children see images of war and death on television screens daily. They need the opportunity to talk, to make art and to play. The task of the adults in their lives is to be honest and open and to reassure the children as much as they are able. Children have an enormous drive to play out their fears. The experience of a parent helping in a classroom with a small group of children aged 5–6 a few days after the twin towers disaster in New York is revealing. There was the opportunity to make a drawing and the children all spontaneously drew towers and buildings on fire and being destroyed. One poignantly had figures jumping from the roof. These particular children were not personally involved in the events, but it was a very emotional time and many people were shocked and horrified. The children had become involved in the feelings, and drawing was their mode of expression. It gave them an opportunity to communicate and to have that communication received.

THE CHILD WHO HAS EXPERIENCED TRAUMA

The children we have in mind are those who have been abused, who have witnessed domestic or other violence or who perhaps have been abandoned. These children can become hypervigilent, permanently on guard, starting at sudden noises. It is likely that these children will not have had the experience of receiving empathy and will therefore be troubled by their feelings. They are also likely to be amongst those who are in need of formal therapeutic help; if so you will need to refer them to an appropriate agency (see page ix).

We hope that at the end of Chapter 4 the children will have learned the following:

◆ *Fear can be helpful and is a normal part of life.*

◆ *Fear affects our bodies in particular ways.*

◆ *Fear will be unhelpful if we get stuck in it.*

Ben felt a buzzing coming up through his legs. He thought he had been trudging through the forest for hours, but he couldn't be sure. Perhaps because he was so tired it was simply his knees that were shaking.

But no! The ground was vibrating! The slimy leaves shivered on their branches, sending little drips flying off their mouldy surface with each quiver. The smell of the forest was almost unbearable now. Ben thought it was like stuffing your head in the kitchen bin. He didn't know how much longer the forest could last. It seemed that sickness was spreading faster and faster. 'Come on,' he said under his breath, looking round for a change of light or some other clue to lead him to the next tribe. 'Where are you?'

Then he saw it. It was about 65 centimetres high, delicate, hovering above the ground. It had no wings, just thin arms that flapped so quickly they managed to lift it into the air. Ben didn't move. He watched the creature flit from tree to tree, darting out from behind one trunk and shooting over to another. It seemed to be anxious, looking for something. Then an alarm rang, like the bell that marked the end of lessons at school. The little figure began to weave in and out of the tree trunks, away from Ben, towards a yellow light in the

distance. Ben followed, but it was hard to keep up. He slid on the slime and once he actually fell, but he didn't let his eyes leave the little figure ahead of him.

It led him to a circle of trees, inside which was a circle of beds – little wooden beds with bright yellow blankets on them and two very puffy pillows each.

Ben found a tree with a wide trunk to hide behind. He was careful not to lean on it, but stood behind it and peeped round. The little creature he had followed shot into the middle of the circle where a group of others stood, wearing pyjamas and holding candlesticks. They were about half as big as the Fumers and the Sobalots and, he thought, half as heavy. They all had thick white hair that reached to their shoulders and bright yellow skin.

When Ben had left the path, just minutes before, he knew it had been morning because the sun had been on its way up in the sky. But from here, although the forest people cast a golden glow from their skin around the circle of beds, it semed dark when he looked back into the forest.

Some of the beds had people in them, tucked in tightly. They didn't look at all sleepy, though. In fact, they looked terrified. Their startled eyes were staring out into the forest. You could see white all round the edges of their blue eyes and their eyebrows, perfect semi-circles, were halfway up their foreheads. Then the one that Ben had followed spoke. 'I'm being followed,' he gasped, in a high, squeaky voice. 'I'd just finished the scary monster watch and was coming back. I *know* I heard footsteps, so there probably is a scary monster out there, and it's coming closer!'

A little group standing in the middle of the beds gasped, their arms started vibrating and they all rose a little in the air. They buzzed round the circle nervously, squinting out into the dark woods. One of them said, 'How will we get a wink of sleep, with this on our minds?' Another said, 'We'll have to send people out in twos for scary monster watch.'

'Yes! Yes!' They all fluttered closer together, like a little swarm.

Then one of them said, 'But no one will get any sleep. *Someone's* got to go to bed, or there'll be no one for us to protect.'

Ben knew they didn't need to be afraid. It was he that the creature had heard. He had to tell them. Ben counted to 3 and then came out from behind the tree. He raised his arm in a kind of wave, hoping it would show them that he was friendly. 'Hello. Please don't be scared. It wasn't a monster, it was me.'

Their look of terror made Ben wonder for a moment if the magic of the forest had turned him into a monster. The yellow from their faces ran down into their necks, leaving them the purest white. The thick hair on their arms and heads moved slowly but surely up. At the sight of Ben, every single white hair on their bodies and heads stood on end. He also heard a 'thump-thump, thump-thump' and realised it was their hearts beating fast because in time with each thump-thump their little chests expanded by a few centimetres. Then every mouth, including the ones belonging to those in bed, opened wide. He heard them all breathe in together, and then they screamed 'aaaaahhhhh!'

Ben quickly looked up and down his own body to make sure he hadn't turned into some hideous beast. He wanted to speak, but there was no way they could have heard him over the din of their screams. He stood very still and put his finger to his lips. When they had stopped and the whole group was hovering in a tight huddle, Ben said in his most reassuring voice, 'There's no need to be afraid of me, I'm just Ben, the human child Rusalka has sent to save the forest. Who are you? Which one is your keeper?'

One of the figures buzzed a little higher in the air than the others. He tapped two others on their shoulders. Both of them jumped and let out a little shriek when he did that. 'You, and you, come with me! It might be a trick!'

The three of them flitted over nearer to Ben. Every now and then their feet would touch the ground, but they would bump back up into the air again. Ben thought it was a good sign that their snow-white hair was slowly coming down from its straight-up-in-the-air position. The heartbeats were not so noisy either. He said, 'Hello. Please don't be afraid. There was no monster, it was me. I was following so I could find you.'

'What do you mean, there's no monster?', squeaked the one Ben thought was the keeper. 'Just because you didn't see it, that doesn't mean it's not there.

That's why it's so scary – we don't know what it looks like!'

'Well, please don't be scared of me. I promise I'm not the monster. I'm here to help. I'm here to save the forest.'

The three looked anxiously at each other and then back at the hovering mass in the middle of the circle of beds. Gradually they all stopped fluttering and landed on the ground, some climbing back into bed, to be tucked in by the others. 'Very well, we'll give you the benefit of the doubt, but please, no sudden moves. They make us very jumpy,' said one of the three near Ben.

The delicate figure stepped forward, his white hair still not quite back to normal. 'My name is Timor, keeper of the Trembolos. Excuse us for not stopping everything to entertain you, but we are all needed to keep watch, and if we're not keeping watch then we're in bed trying to get some sleep.'

Now Timor was up close; Ben noticed that his body was quivering, as if he had just stepped out of a swimming pool. 'But it's not bed-time, is it?' asked Ben.

'We have to do it in shifts, so it's always bed-time for some of us. We have a round-the-clock rota. That way, there's always people to keep watch.'

'Has anyone ever been hurt by the monster?' Their nervousness was starting to make Ben feel edgy. They kept looking over his shoulder to the dark forest and he found he was starting to do the same.

'Not yet, no,' said Timor shaking his head quickly.

'Has anyone *ever* seen it?' asked Ben.

'No, not yet, no.' Timor shook his head again.

'So you've got to admit, there might not be a monster at all?'

'But there might be. We could never stop watching, because you never know.'

Ben didn't know what to say. He felt sorry for the Trembolos, always afraid and always at bed-time – what a horrible combination!

Ben glanced back at the circle of beds and saw a Trembolo diving under one of the beds, his bottom sticking up in the air. He came back up and said to the Trembolo sitting up in that bed, 'Definitely no monster under the bed, at the moment.' The Trembolo in the bed lay back down on the pillow, still looking anxious, and pulled the yellow blankets right up to her chin.

A Trembolo scurried over with a tiny mug of hot chocolate for Ben. It had spilt over his arm because he was trembling so much. 'Here, we made an extra hot chocolate. Do have one.'

'Thank you,' said Ben. He reached out a little too quickly, frightening the Trembolo back up into the air again. All the Trembolos in bed were being handed a mug, but most of the chocolate was spilling on their bed-covers because all their hands shook so.

Ben was glad to see that Timor had both feet on the ground, but he noticed that he was still looking out into the forest. Ben put a hand on his quivering shoulder. 'Timor, I think that if you have never seen the monster, you should all go to bed at the same time and have just one watch team on for the night. Then, after a week, if no one's seen anything, you could watch for it every other night, and then maybe once a week. Eventually, you might find you don't need any monster watch to be able to get to sleep.'

The Trembolos' eyebrows moved up to the very tops of their heads. Timor waved the others back to the circle and then came closer. Ben could see that even his eye-lashes shook from all his trembling. 'Are you telling me that when you go to sleep at night, there is no scary monster watch, at all?' he asked in a whisper.

'Yep,' said Ben, feeling rather brave.

'But what if you wake up and worry about the monster? If nobody's on watch, how can you get back to sleep?'

All their talk of the invisible scary monster had seemed quite silly to Ben, but when Timor asked him that, he suddenly didn't feel quite so brave. He wanted to say that he just closed his eyes and went back to sleep. He liked appearing brave and bold. But Ben was clever. He had learnt that when he was honest about his feelings, the keepers had decided to give him their pieces of the Spectrum. If he lied, Timor might not give him his piece. He said, 'Well, I take a deep breath and tell myself the next time I breathe I will be in my mum and dad's bed and I'll be safe. Then I run for it – out of bed, across the room, over the landing and into their room.'

But last night, Ben remembered, it hadn't been that easy. He hadn't been able to open his parents' door straightaway. He thought they'd locked him out, then he thought maybe the monster in his dream had got to his parents first and was waiting for him on the other side of the door. As Ben remembered this, his scalp and skin felt as if they were being pricked by a million pins. He watched the hairs on his arms stand up, and he reached to touch his hair – it was the same. His whole body was quivering, just like Timor's. Ben was shaking and his heart was beating loudly in time with Timor's.

'Then what happened?' said Timor from just above the ground, his hair standing up like stalagmites.

'Well, I pushed the door a bit harder and it opened. My dad's shoe was behind it, that's why it was hard for me to get in. I ran into the bed and got in the gap between Mum and Dad. Then I knew it was OK. But it took a while for my breathing to slow down again.'

Timor jolted back to the ground. 'Phew!' he said. 'Close call.' A drop of leaf slime landed on the top of Timor's white head. Timor wiped it with his sleeve, his nose crinkled up because of the smell.

'If I were you, Timor,' said Ben, looking at the dripping tree, 'there's something I'd be more worried about than a monster.'

'What?' gasped Timor, all a-quiver again.

'I would be scared that the forest was going to die and I'd have nowhere to live.'

Timor's arms started flapping and he rose above the ground, turning to the anxious group behind him. 'Yes! Yes! You're right! Everyone! Panic stations! The forest is going to die. We'll all be homeless! *We're* going to die!'

At that, the Trembolos who were in bed got up, and darted around the circle, hair on end, hearts beating, vibrating and bouncing off each other, shouting, 'Homeless! Dead! We're all going to be homeless and dead!'

'But listen!' shouted Ben. 'You can do something about this. Give me your piece of the Spectrum and I think it will be OK.'

It seemed that the air was full of flitting, fluttering Trembolos. Timor came back over to Ben. 'It's all very well you being a human child that Rusalka has sent, but I've not been without my piece of the Spectrum for two hundred years. I'm scared of what might happen. I'm scared of being without it.'

'It's like me having to take a deep breath when I run to my parents' bed,' said Ben. 'Breathe in and do what you know you've got to do. Anything's got to be better than always being so scared. Come on, Timor, be brave.'

'Me? Brave? Trembolos aren't brave, Ben, or we wouldn't be Trembolos.'

Ben started to panic himself. He *had* to get the piece, and quickly. The forest was getting worse by the minute. 'Come on, Timor, give it to me. You have to give it to me.'

Timor looked out into the dark forest, but his hair stayed flat and his trembling was only a slight quiver. He reached down the neck of his pyjama top and pulled out a thong that was hanging round his neck. There was the piece of crystal, only it didn't look as crystal should. It looked like a jelly, a wobbly lump. When Timor handed it over though, Ben felt the hard coldness of the crystal in his hand.

All the Trembolos flitted around Ben, darting and buzzing close by him, stroking him cautiously on the head. Timor took a deep breath and said, 'Go, Ben! Restore the Spectrum. Don't worry about the scary monster watch – we'll handle that!'

Overall aim To learn about fear; how sometimes it is helpful, how it feels in our bodies and how sometimes it stops us enjoying life.

ROUND 1

Aim To warm up, make contact and have fun.

Pass a surprise All stand in a circle holding hands. The teacher makes a surprised face at the child on their right. When that child sees the surprise, they make a surprised face at the child on their right and so on. After one round, the surprise can be passed to the left instead. Next time round, two surprises can be sent travelling in different directions round the circle.

ROUND 2

Aim To allow non-verbal disclosure.

All change The teacher instructs children who have similar feelings to exchange places. For example:

◆ *Change places everybody who sometimes feels scared of the dark.*

◆ *Change places everybody who sometimes feels scared of being lost.*

◆ *Change places everybody who sometimes feels scared of being hurt.*

ROUND 3

Aim To engage with the story and think about fear, particularly about when it helps us and when it doesn't.

Question What happens to the Trembolos when they are scared?

Question What happens in your body when you feel scared?

Try to allow each child to answer both questions if they want.

ROUND 4

Aim To learn about fear.

Using a flipchart divided into two columns as before, hold a discussion about fear. For 'How can fear help us?' you can pepper the conversation with ideas such as 'to keep us safe', 'it protects us', 'it stops us doing dangerous things'. The responses to 'How can fear be unhelpful?' might include 'it can make us anxious all the time', 'it can stop us having fun', 'it can stop us trying new things'.

ROUND 5

Aim To move towards closure.

Open forum to hear any further thoughts or last words.

Ask if anyone would like to say anything else about fear or the Trembolos.

ROUND 6

Aim To close.

Duck, duck, goose

Everyone stands in a circle. One person walks around the outside of the circle and touches people on the shoulder. They say, 'Duck, duck, duck' (they can choose how many times they say 'duck') and then they say 'goose'. When the child touches someone and says 'goose', they both have to run around the circle in opposite directions, trying to get back to the vacant space. The last person to get back to the space walks round outside the circle and starts the game again.

CREATIVE ACTIVITY 1

Make a shaker

You will need an assortment of plastic containers such as yoghurt pots, bottles and boxes; some lentils or rice; some larger dried beans such as butter beans, elastic bands; paper, ready-mix paint and PVA glue.

The children put some rice or beans into a container. The top is closed with a piece of paper and secured with an elastic band. The shaker is then decorated with ready-mix paint mixed with PVA glue. It can be used in creative activity 2.

CREATIVE ACTIVITY 2

Percussion and dance

This music activity is designed to enable children to explore the emotion of fear freely. You may choose to do this activity with smaller groups, which could then come together for a larger performance after the group work.

You will need percussion instruments, especially shakers, and space for all the children to move about. This activity can follow a rereading of the passage starting *'I'm being followed he gasped,'* on page 41 and ending *'Please don't be scared. It wasn't a monster, it was me.'* on page 41. Dance is a particularly useful activity for anxious children as it allows them to rehearse safely, moving from flight to fight.

Invite the children to explore the instruments and notice what each sounds like. Allow a few minutes for this. Ask them to imagine the sounds the Trembolos would make. Help them by asking questions about the sounds: loud or quiet, low or high, buzzy or rumbly, tinkly or squeaky and so on. Lots of noise is fine.

The children are invited to be Trembolos, making Trembolo sounds and buzzing and darting around the room. Each child chooses the instrument they would like to play. Encourage them to use all the space in the room. As before, you can draw a picture (or lines) on the floor in chalk and get them to dance over the lines.

To bring this activity to a close, begin to conduct them with arm movements, lowering the volume and bringing the music to an end. Play some calming, soothing music to close.

CREATIVE ACTIVITY 3

Trembolo puppet

You will need the Trembolo's face on page 84 copied onto card, paints, felt pens and lolly sticks.

Invite the children to cut out the face and to colour it. The Trembolo can be attached to a lolly stick to make a simple puppet. Ask the children to name their puppet.

The children could role play a scene with their puppet in which a Trembolo has come out of the forest and is visiting their classroom for the day. They can explore what the Trembolo thinks of their world.

CREATIVE ACTIVITY 4

Worry doll

You will need old-fashioned wooden pegs, felt pens, PVA glue, short lengths of thick wool or rug yarn, scraps of cloth.

The children dress the peg as a Trembolo, drawing a face onto the head and using wool to make standing-up hair.

The finished Trembolo is kept in a safe place. When the child is anxious about something, they can tell their worry to the doll, who will do the worrying for them. (This idea comes from Guatemalean worry dolls that people keep under their pillows to deal with their anxieties.)

The tribe of fearful feelings

fright

terror

fear

dread

anxiety

qualm

wariness

scared

nervous

phobia

panic

concern

Jealous feelings are very common amongst small children, especially those with siblings. Cries of 'Unfair', 'Her's is bigger', 'He's got more than me' are common.

Imagine for a moment the following scenario. Your partner comes home from work one day and announces that they love you very much – so much, in fact, that they are going to have another partner and you are all going to live happily together. Imagine your feelings. They probably include hurt, anger, rejection, loss, sadness, insecurity, deprivation, fear, anxiety, shame, unworthiness and feeling unlovely and unlovable.

This imaginary scenario is not a million miles away from the experience of a child dethroned by the birth of a new baby brother or sister. If this is the current or recent experience of a child in your class then the story of the Notfers may resonate powerfully and you will need to be alert and sensitive to this. Other common situations in which jealous feelings are often to the fore are step-families.

Jealousy is a complex emotion encompassing many flavours. It is a secondary rather than a primary emotion. It would be helpful to remind yourself of the notes on anger and sadness (pages 11–12 and page 26) before working with this chapter.

Jealousy in siblings often manifests itself in squabbling over food, toys and treats. When jealousy is persistent and entrenched, then the objects that are fought over may symbolise parental love. Many feelings of jealousy arise in the ordinary rough and tumble or squelchiness of family life because it is simply not possible to treat each child in an identical way. Learning about sameness and difference and sharing are essential social lessons in life, and dealing with jealousy is part and parcel of everyday life. Ordinarily if a child is able to express how they feel, they will be met by understanding and the reassurance that they are indeed loved.

Sadly there will be some children for whom the tragic reality is indeed that they are not the favoured child. For example, the experience of the little girl who would lie in bed alone night after night, having been given a most cursory goodnight, listening to her mother playing and laughing with her more favoured sister. We may not be able to change the situation at home, but we can help with the feelings of the rejected child.

Jealousy, like all painful feelings, is more bearable when allowed expression with a safe person and when that person can understand and empathise even though they are unable to change the situation. It can be a huge relief for a child to be heard and understood, and to be no longer alone with the pain.

By the end of working on this chapter we hope that the children will have learned the following:

◆ *Jealousy is normal, everyone feels it sometimes.*

◆ *Jealousy is a complicated feeling.*

There were so many dead leaves on the ground that Ben's feet squelched and slid with every step. Whenever he slipped, he reached out to grab a tree and regretted it the minute his hand closed round a weak branch. They cried out in pain. One branch couldn't take his weight and came away from the trunk, squealing with distress and fear. It shrivelled up and died in Ben's hand. He laid it gently to one side of the path and covered it with some old leaves. The smell was so bad, his eyes watered. He walked with his hand over his nose and mouth. Splodges of colour on the floor were all that was left of any flowers and not a single tree could stand up on its own. At least he had only one more piece of the Spectrum to find. He could feel the weight of the three pieces in the purse hung around his neck, hidden under his shirt. He was sure they were getting heavier, but he was exhausted and it was hard to be sure.

He jumped. The pieces of the Spectrum had moved in the purse, and his chest was suddenly warm. He pulled the leather thong on which it hung out of his T-shirt and opened the purse. Rays of bright light, red and blue and yellow, shot out of the purse with such force that he moved his head out of the way in case they hit him. Nervously, he turned the purse upside down to let the three pieces of the Spectrum fall into his hand. They continued to send out rays of pure red, yellow and blue. Ben wasn't sure if he was imagining it, but they seemed to be warm in his hand.

It must know! It's getting ready to be the Spectrum again, thought Ben excitedly. He put them back carefully in the purse, and put the purse under his T-shirt. 'Right,' he said under his breath, looking round for a change of light or some other strange thing that was starting to seem normal. 'Where *are* you?'

Sure enough, to his left, through the saggy black trunks, Ben saw a soft green glow. It wasn't a bright light, but it was a light all the same, so he left the path and walked towards it. The ground was uneven and he stumbled over enormous squidgy roots that seemed to be breaking through the ground in search of some air. With each step he took, the light grew brighter and greener and Ben started to feel sick. Just when he was wondering about putting his finger down his throat to get it over and done with, he heard the sound for the first time. 'Ching! Ching! Ching! Ting-a-ling-ling!'

Triangles! He could hear triangles! Why would anyone play the triangle in the forest? The ching, ching, ching and ting-a-ling-ling died down, as high-pitched, squeaky voices started yelling and yelping. He couldn't hear what the voices were shouting, but he knew from the squawking and screeching that there were lots of them. He was concentrating so hard on trying to hear what the voices were saying, he forgot to look where he was going and trod on a particularly big root. He flew forward and rolled over and over on the boggy ground. In the green blur that got brighter with each head over heels, the sharp voices got louder and hurt his ears. He came to a sudden halt when his feet struck a tree stump. He sat up and rubbed his filthy head.

Just ahead was a circle of trees that propped each other up. When he looked at the trees, flashing lights made him squint so that his eyes were half-shut. On every branch of every tree dangled tiny triangular mirrors.

Inside the circle, hordes of elf-like creatures dashed around noisily. Their heads were no bigger than grapefruits, but they had enormous pointed ears whose tips reached above their heads.

They looked younger than the Trembolos and Sobalots, but their hair was silver. They wore red and white striped trousers, and leather tunics with wide leather belts which had objects hanging from them. At first glance Ben didn't know what the objects were – except one, which he saw was a small silver triangle. Each person stood no taller than Ben's waist, and each one was part of the reason Ben had felt sick. The light in the forest was coming from their skin, which was vivid green.

In their hussle and bussle they hadn't even noticed Ben's bumpy arrival, so he sat and watched in silence. In the centre of the clearing were dozens of triangular tables. The elf-like people were scurrying about, setting the tables for a meal. They worked in threes: in some groups one laid the knife, one the fork, and the third measured the distance between the two. Every so often a squabble broke out, and the knife or fork was moved a tiny distance up or down, to the left or to the right. Other teams were pouring drinks. One would put the cup down, the next would pour and the third would measure the amount of drink in the cup. When a squabble really got going, one or more of them would hit their triangle hard and shout 'Not fair, not fair!' Then something shocking happened. If Ben hadn't noticed it, he might have sat there unseen for a lot longer. But he did notice it, and it gave him such a fright that he screamed before he could stop himself. And when he screamed all the little green people heard him and then they *all* did the same shocking thing and Ben had to put his hand over his mouth, so he wouldn't scream again.

Ben had been watching two of the creatures talking. It looked as if they were about to have a serious fight. They were shouting at each other and dingling

their triangles with all their might. Then, without any warning, the smaller of the two spun his head round – all the way round! That was when he noticed it wasn't just their skin that was bright green. It was their eyes too. When

Ben shrieked, every head there span round and round until it found who had made such a strange, deep noise. After all the shouting, chattering and ding-a-linging, the silence was noisy.

'Hello,' said Ben. 'Hello!' they all said back at him at once, startled.

'Are you the child that has come to save our forest?' said one of them, turning his body so it faced the same way as his head (this was a big relief to Ben).

'Yes,' said Ben.

A smile broke across all the green faces at once, and all their bodies turned to face the same way as their heads. They held out their short arms to him and he knew he was meant to walk into the circle. 'Welcome,' said the one who had asked him the question. 'We're the Notfers. Come, sit down and eat with us. I am Vigil, keeper of the Notfers.'

He walked over to Ben and shook his hand. Ben saw how thin Vigil's hand was, and that made him notice how very thin all of Vigil's body was, and then how thin all of the Notfers were. Vigil looked up at Ben with a big smile, his green eyes twinkling, and then he span his head round twice before shouting, 'Someone get the boy a triangle so he can eat. Quick!'

Ben sat on the rickety wooden stool that Vigil pointed to. 'Why do I need a triangle to eat?'

'So you can sound the alarm, of course.'

A Notfer ran up and slapped a leather belt on the table in front of him. Not only was there a triangle hanging from it, but also a red funnel with a dish attached to it, a tiny microscope, a tape measure, a weighing scale and a magnifying glass the size of a penny. 'Put it on, put it on,' Vigil said impatiently. 'You'll need it.'

A Notfer appeared at the table with a wooden plate, piled high with mashed potato, peas and sausages. On a smaller plate was a quivering mound of green jelly.

'What's all this for?' asked Ben, trying to put the belt on and holding in his tummy because it was too small for him. He realised now that he was very hungry indeed, and wanted to eat his food right away.

Vigil leant over to the belt that was now strapped round Ben's waist and gently touched each item. 'This,' he said tapping the funnel-shaped object, 'is your pea counter, this scale is to weigh the potato and jelly, the measuring tape is to measure your juice and sausage, and this, of course,' he said, tinging the triangle, 'is your alarm.' Without giving Ben the chance to ask the questions he wanted to put about the microscope and magnifying glass, Vigil stood on the table, clapped his hands and shouted. 'Eat!'

A cheer went up and Ben did as he was told. The food tasted good and for a few moments he didn't even look around him. He was halfway through his second sausage, having eaten the first one, all his peas and most of the potato, before he looked up and realised he was the only one sitting down. On his left, two Notfers were pouring peas through a funnel; to his right, big dollops of potato were being dropped onto a scale; triangles were dinging in every direction, along with the cry he was quickly getting used to: 'Not fair! Not fair! Not fair!'

When the Notfers *did* eat, they kept doing the thing Ben wished they wouldn't do. They'd spin their heads round and round until their green eyes fixed on something that might not be fair and then they would run over and start another whole new argument – about peas, or potato, or jelly, or juice. He also noticed that they kept glancing in the hanging mirrors, which enabled them to see round corners. Ben finished his meal long before all the others. When Vigil finally sat back down next to him his plate was nearly empty even though he hadn't eaten a single mouthful. Ben noticed that if the alarm was sounded and it was found that you had more food than someone else, you had to put half of it in a big dustbin. Ben wondered if this was why they were all so thin.

It was then that Ben spotted the green glass triangle dangling from Vigil's belt. 'Vigil, I need your piece of the Spectrum – that's it, isn't it?' Ben nodded at Vigil's belt. Rusalka told me you would give it to me.'

'Not yet, not yet, little boy. All in good time,' said Vigil through a mouthful of peas.

Ben thought it was a bit of a cheek calling him *little* boy. His feet could touch the ground, whereas Vigil's were swinging in mid-air, his short legs only half as long as Ben's.

'Vigil, I haven't much time. Please give me your piece of the Spectrum. You don't want the forest to die, do you?'

'If the forest dies, we all die, but I can't give it to someone who's not one of us. Look at you! You're not green, your ears are a funny round shape, your eyes dawdle and look at the same thing for too long and your head doesn't swivel very far!'

'Rusalka sent me! Isn't that good enough?' Ben was getting desperate.

'I'm not handing my piece of the Spectrum over to someone I don't know. It would be irresponsible. I need to ask you questions too. It's not fair if I don't get to ask you things, is it?'

'Go on, then. I'm all ears.' Ben was trying not to show how impatient he was feeling.

'Yes, rather strange ones, if you ask me.'

'It depends on where you're from, Vigil. Where I come from people don't have pointed ears. Mine are quite normal. I'd get laughed at if I had ears like you.'

Vigil stroked the sharp tip of one ear with his finger while his head swivelled round a couple of times, rather more slowly than usual. 'Strange,' he muttered quietly to himself. 'Very strange.' His green eyes stared ahead, instead of darting all over the place. 'What else is different in your forest?'

Ben laughed, 'I don't live in a forest, Vigil. I live in a house, in a street.'

Vigil suddenly stared at Ben's T-shirt, then looked at the bits of toggle-like twig on his own leather tunic. 'I have to use fasten-ups. Why don't you? Why are you such a show off?'

'I'm not,' said Ben starting to get annoyed. 'That's just the way T-shirts are. Do you spend your *whole* time comparing yourself and what you've got with other people?'

'What else is there to do?' said Vigil, leaning down to measure the length of Ben's trainer, and then his own foot.

'There are lots of other things to do, Vigil, lots and lots of stuff that is much more fun,' said Ben, pulling his shoe away from the measuring tape.

Vigil frowned. 'Nothing could be more fun than getting one more pea than everyone else at tea. Or being the one to spot that someone else has got it and taking it off them.'

'Oh, Vigil! What does it matter if a Notfer has one more pea?

'It matters, Ben,' said Vigil looking shocked, his head whizzing round so fast that his face went all blurry, 'because Notfers believe if you have more than everyone else, you are special. If you have less than everyone else, you are not.'

'But if you've got more peas than everyone else, you have to give half of them away! You end up worse off!'

Vigil twiddled his thumbs for a minute. 'Do you really mean to tell me that you don't count peas where you come from?' Vigil was still for the first time since they'd met. His eyes looked straight into Ben's.

'That's right, and we don't weigh potato or jelly, or measure our juice.'

Vigil gasped and covered his mouth with both spindly hands. 'But how do you know it's *fair*?' he shrieked, leaning forward and quickly counting the holes in Ben's belt before counting his own.

'We don't, I suppose, but it's near enough so it doesn't matter.'

'So, Ben, if a Notfer in your house had more potato than you, you wouldn't sound the alarm?'

'No, and anyway we don't have an alarm.'

Vigil scratched his head. 'So Notfers in your house never get to sound the alarm?'

Ben was about to say no, but then he remembered what had happened last Christmas. He remembered ripping up his Advent calendar because it didn't have any sweets in it. He remembered grabbing the sweets from Anna's stupid Barbie calendar and running upstairs as he stuffed them into his mouth. He was silent for a moment, and then he said, 'Sometimes, if something is *really* unfair, we shout, or cry, or,' he paused, looking at the forest floor, realising how bad this must sound to Vigil, 'steal things.' He looked up and was surprised to see Vigil grinning from one pointed ear to the other.

'There you are then!' he said, with a sharp clap of his hands.

'What?'

'Look at you, Ben, you're one of us!' Vigil had leapt down from his seat and was pulling Ben over to one of the mirrors hanging from a tree. Ben looked into the mirror while Vigil chuckled and slapped his hands on his bony thighs. Ben saw his own *green* eyes glaring back at him, touched his green skin, and pulled his pointed ears, horrified.

'You're a Notfer, you're a Notfer.' Vigil turned and scampered back to the tables to where the others were pushing jelly through a special sieve. 'Come and look at Ben, he's a Notfer now!'

Ben could see in his mirror that they were all running over to him, as fast as they could, each terrified of getting there last. He turned round to face the line of emerald eyes looking at him. He waited for the cheer, or a chant of 'Notfer, Notfer', but instead all their smiles fell. They looked disappointed.

Vigil ran up to him and wiped Ben's cheek with his hand. 'What's happened?' he asked. 'You've turned back. Your skin's gone all white, and your ears have gone back to weird.' Ben span round and looked again in the mirror.

He was back to normal. He put his hands onto Vigil's bony shoulders.

'Vigil, I'm not a Notfer, but sometimes I know what it's like to be one. And you, Vigil, are a Notfer, but now you know what it's like in my world. I think we've got to know each other, don't you?'

There was a load groan behind them. Ben and Vigil turned to see all the trees in the circle collapse onto the floor. Vigil looked down at his belt and unhooked the crystal triangle. He tilted it between his stocky little finger and thumb so it caught the light and flashed at them. 'Here you are, Ben. Go and save our forest.'

Ben took the triangle and held it firmly in his hand. 'Thanks for tea,' he shouted back at them. 'Next time we eat together, maybe you won't need to sound the alarm at all.'

The Notfers thought this was very funny and he could hear their squeaky laughs while he found his way back to the dirt path.

Ben felt the humming next to his chest. The Spectrum pieces were moving again. He held the final piece in his hand until he was alone again. What should he do now? The piece Vigil had just given him was humming, and the pieces in the purse were jiggling against his chest. He was afraid. He didn't know what would happen when he put the pieces back together. He sat on a tree trunk. In his right hand was Vigil's triangle, in his left hand was the vibrating leather pouch. What now?

He heard and felt her coming before he saw her. His hair moved in the wind and his ears were filled with the rhythmic beating of enormous wings. Rusalka!

Overall aim To learn about jealousy.

ROUND 1

Aim To warm up, make contact, have fun.

Pass a hi-five All stand in a circle. The teacher greets the child on their right with a gentle hi-five. The child passes the greeting onto the child on their right and so on. The greeting is passed round the circle. Next time two hi-fives can be sent in opposite directions round the circle to greet everyone.

ROUND 2

Aim To engage with the story and think about jealousy. The questions encourage self-awareness in the children.

Question What do you think is funny about the Notfers?

Question Can you tell us a time when you felt like Ben when he took the sweets from his sister's Advent calendar? How did you feel?

If possible, each child should have the opportunity to answer one question – ideally both. It is important that each child's emotional disclosure is met with an empathic response. This can be made by one of the group, but if it isn't then you need to acknowledge and receive the feeling (see page vii). This models to the children how to respond to feelings.

ROUND 3

Aim To learn about jealousy.

Ask the children what jealousy feels like and write up their responses on a flipchart. They might say things like 'hurt', 'angry', 'afraid of losing someone', 'little', 'mean', 'lonely', 'unloved' and so on. You can comment that jealousy is not like the other feelings we have met so far in the book and that it is a mixture of things.

ROUND 4

Aim To move towards closure.

Open forum to hear any further thoughts or last words.

Ask if there is anything anyone would like to say or ask about jealousy or the Notfers.

ROUND 5

Aim To close.

The storm

All sit in a circle with both feet flat on the ground. The teacher tells the story of a storm and invites the children to join in with the sounds and actions.

Once upon a time there was a forest and the wind rustled through the trees.

This is accompanied by rubbing the palms of the hands together to make a rustling noise.

Then it began to rain.

This is accompanied by gentle finger clicking.

Then it rained a little harder.

Louder finger clicking moving to hand clapping, slowly becoming faster and louder.

Now it begins to thunder.

Feet stamping as well as loud clapping reaches a crescendo, then begins to slow and lessen.

The storm passes.

The children are taken back through the sounds and actions to the rustling in the forest.

The storm is over.

CREATIVE ACTIVITY 1

Music and movement

This music activity is designed to enable children to explore the emotion of jealousy freely and spontaneously. It may be better to do this activity with smaller groups; that will depend on how familiar the children are with the thoughtful use of instruments, musical composition and role play. The small groups could come together for a larger performance.

You will need a range of musical instruments and space for the children to move about. This activity can follow a rereading the passage starting '*Put it on, put it on,*' on page 56 to *glancing in the hanging mirrors, which enabled them to see round corners* on page 57.

Invite the children to explore the instruments and notice what each sounds like for a few minutes. Ask them to imagine the sounds a Notfer orchestra would make. Help them develop their ideas by asking questions about the sounds, loud or quiet, low or high, scratchy or rumbly, tinkly or squeaky and so on.

Invite the children to play some Notfer music. Each child then chooses the instrument they would like to play. Some or all of the children might want to move with their instruments; this can be encouraged. Bring this to a close by joining in as the conductor. Lower the volume and bring the orchestra to silence.

You can extend this activity by including a reading from the chapter, encouraging the children to join in with sound effects and actions – for example, Ben walking, falling, the Notfers measuring. Read the story a second time, encouraging big, exaggerated sounds and actions.

CREATIVE ACTIVITY 2

Paint a leaf

You will need large smooth leaves, ready-mix paints, PVA glue and brushes.

Ask the children to paint a Notfer face on a large leaf. Have a leaf already painted to give them the idea. Ask them to give their Notfer a name. Use paint mixed with PVA glue to stop it flaking off the leaf.

CREATIVE ACTIVITY 3

Notfer puppet

You will need the Notfer template on page 85, copied onto card, paints, felt pens and lolly sticks.

The children cut out the template and colour the Notfer face. The face can be attached to a lolly stick with glue to make a simple puppet. Ask the children to name their puppet.

The children imagine that they are Ben entering the forest and meeting the Notfers. The puppet gives them an opportunity to interview a Notfer and find out more about them.

CREATIVE ACTIVITY 4

Notfer tea-time

You will need Play-Doh® and a tea set, scales and measures.

This is an opportunity for the children to play at being Notfers. Invite them to make Play-Doh® peas, sausages, mash and jelly. They can measure out juice, weigh potatoes, measure sausages, count peas and practise dividing.

This activity could lend itself to numeracy work.

The tribe of jealous feelings

envy

rivalry

jealousy

desirous

covetous

possessive

insecure

mistrust

In this chapter the forest is restored to full health amid much delight and celebration.

Joy and happiness are significant feelings and it is just as vital that they are acknowledged and affirmed as more uncomfortable feelings. Laughing enhances flexible, creative and complex thinking (Goleman 1996). Telling jokes in the classroom has its benefits. Studies have shown that more neural connections are made when a person is feeling happy. The implication here is that happy children learn better. We are hard wired to play, especially to rough-and-tumble play. The impulse to play comes from spontaneous neural urges within the brain. It is not superfluous. All young mammals engage in play.

Scientific evidence aside, we all know about play. It is fun, intensely joyful, voluntary and spontaneous, and all children need to engage in play. The United Nations has proclaimed play to be a universal and inalienable right of childhood (Landreth 2002). The trouble with play is that it is noisy, boisterous and exuberant, and sometimes adults find it difficult to cope with.

We intend to imply that Ben has met and befriended his feelings. By association the children can do the same. This happens when the feelings are listened to and acknowledged – the Wisdom Speaker sends for the keepers before the Spectrum can be healed. In the story the whole is more than the sum of the parts. This is true in life; emotional well-being is the access to a range of emotions.

We also intend the story to provide a tool for the children. Just as Ben thinks affectionately of Volka when he becomes angry and the thought helps him deal with his anger cleanly, the children in the classroom can think of Volka, Terpia, Vigil and Timor when they experience such emotions.

By the end of working through this book, we hope the children will have learned that:

◆ *to be human is to experience a rich range of emotions;*

◆ *joy, play and laughter are hugely important;*

◆ *being familiar with and befriending your feelings helps you to be confident and secure in yourself.*

Ben had to squint to see Rusalka through the swirling reds and blues, oranges and greens. The colours sparkled and fizzed as they span around her beating wings. Ben laughed with relief and delight. He had got all the pieces of the Spectrum and Rusalka had not abandoned him.

He waved his arms at her as she hovered in the air, big and strong, but graceful as a swan. 'Look, Rusalka! Look! I've got them all!'

She landed softly and quietly as a butterfly in front of Ben. In one gentle move she reached down and lifted him into her hand, level with her smiling face. 'You did it, Ben! You are the best human child there ever was and I will love you for ever.' He didn't know what to say, so he beamed back at her and blushed a bit.

Then, suddenly, Rusalka looked over Ben's shoulder and across her forehead appeared a frown so deep and wide that he believed he could have walked in it. Ben turned round and realised why she looked worried. 'It's got worse, hasn't it, Rusalka? It seems to be speeding up.'

'I badly want to hear all about Volka and Terpia, Vigil and Timor,' said Rusalka, 'but I fear that if we don't restore the Spectrum right now, it will be too late. Oh Ben, the forest looks dead already!'

Ben lifted the purse up high so it was right in front of her eyes. 'Here they are, Rusalka. What do I do now?'

'You put them together, Ben, but I must put you down first. There will be very strong magic at work. I'm not sure what will happen.'

Ben didn't like hearing Rusalka say this. He thought she would know exactly what was going to happen. She lowered him to the floor and stood next to him. 'Don't worry. I will scoop you up immediately if you need to get out of the way. I won't let anything hurt you.' Now he was even more worried. It hadn't occurred to him that putting the Spectrum together would be dangerous. Rusalka stood up straight, towering above Ben. 'We have no time to waste. Do it! Restore the Spectrum and save the forest!'

Ben put the purse on the ground and laid the pieces on it. They didn't move. They didn't hum or glow. They simply lay there, colourless and still. Ben lifted Volka's lightning bolt and placed it next to Terpia's teardrop, then he got Vigil's triangle and Timor's splodge and laid them next to the others. Nervously, he cupped his hand round all of them and pushed them towards each other, his eyes half-closed, ready for an explosion or a crack of lightning.

But nothing happened. The Spectrum pieces sat like any old pieces of glass. Rusalka and Ben stared. All they could hear was the drip, drip, drip of rot falling from leaves into the rank puddles on the ground, and the distant screams of falling trees. Ben looked from the Spectrum up into Rusalka's enormous green eyes. They were like lakes, filled with tears. 'It's too late, Ben. The magic isn't working. The Spectrum is never going to be restored. The forest won't survive.'

Ben couldn't believe it. He had done everything that had been asked of him. Even when he was tired, or hungry, or afraid, he hadn't let anything get in the way of collecting the four pieces. He looked round at the forest. It was no more than a stinking graveyard. Rusalka bowed her big, beautiful head and cried. Without looking up she held out her hand and Ben climbed onto her lap, his own eyes blurred with tears. Rusalka held Ben close to her face and together they wept. Ben held on tightly, for fear he would be swept away with the torrents of coloured water flowing down Rusalka's face. His own tears dropped their tiny droplets into hers and they all flowed down together. Neither of them noticed (they were too busy being sad), but their tears knew exactly where to go. They hurried down her cheeks, and off her chin into the silver bowl around her neck.

When the bowl was full, and when Rusalka and Ben were quiet from all their crying, the tears started to swirl and twist and race round and round the bowl, faster and faster until the colours merged and the liquid was completely black and completely still. Rusalka only realised what was happening when the black liquid in the bowl started to bubble and spit and spattered their faces with shiny black flecks.

'Ben! The Wisdom Speaker!' As quickly and carefully as she could, Rusalka put Ben down, took the bowl from around her neck and placed it next to him. They watched the surface grow calm and flat. The black faded to grey, then white and then it was perfectly clear. Ben and Rusalka leant their faces close enough to see their reflections and let their breath blow ripples on the surface.

The Wisdom Speaker appeared suddenly, so crisp and clear that Ben forgot that he was looking into a bowl of tears. It's a face as old as the world itself, thought Ben. Rusalka jumped at the sight of it. 'Wisdom Speaker! I found the human child and he found the keepers and he collected the four pieces of the Spectrum – like you said, but the magic won't work. I think we are too late.'

Rusalka started sobbing again – awful, hopeless sobs that Ben couldn't bear to hear. He leant closer to the edge of the bowl and stared into the dark ebony eyes. They were surrounded by wrinkles like crumpled tissue paper, but they were lively and strong.

Ben's heart leapt as the Wisdom Speaker looked him straight in the eye. It felt like a dart of electricity shooting through his body. The thin lips turned a little at the corners and the eyes softened. Then the face turned back to Rusalka. 'Rusalka, in your hurry to save your forest, you failed to understand one important thing. You need the *keepers* as well as their pieces of the Spectrum. You are all needed to put the Spectrum back together. Together, you can make the magic that is needed.'

Even with all his concentration on the bowl, Ben could hear the trees falling and groaning all round them. He didn't know if it was polite for a human child to talk to the Wisdom Speaker, but he couldn't help himself. 'Have we got time? Isn't it too late?'

The face in the water looked at Ben and said, 'Time *is* short, but while there is a breath of life left, it is worth trying, isn't it?'

Rusalka seemed to come back to life herself. 'Yes! Yes, it is. We shall go now. Thank you, Wisdom Speaker.' The waters started swirling, and Rusalka grabbed the bowl and gulped down its contents. Then she tipped the last drips into Ben's mouth. 'Come on, Ben, and hold tight. Let's get those keepers – and fast.'

Ben had to close his eyes against the rush of wind in his face. He clung onto the lining of Rusalka's pocket as tightly as he possibly could.

In all the flying Rusalka had done, from one world to another, across the dark spaces in between worlds – where if you are not careful you can fall into black holes of nothingness – she had never flown so fast and so low. There were

barely any trees still standing. The ground was shaking with earth tremors every few minutes. Fires had sprung up everywhere. The smell of smoke and death made Ben feel sick and his throat tightened. Forest people were running around frantically, crying and screaming, with their hands on their heads.

Then Ben thought *he* was going to die. His head felt as if it was going to explode. Surely this was the end of the forest and the end of him? But it wasn't, it was only Rusalka. She had taken a deep breath and was shouting the names of the keepers. Her voice was low, like the thunder, but it crackled through the air like lightning. 'Volka! Terpia! Vigil! Timor!'

Again and again she shook the forest with her call. Eventually, Ben dared to peep out of Rusalka's pocket, covering his ears as firmly as he could. Everywhere he looked, forest people were running for cover under fallen branches, down holes in the ground, into hollow tree trunks. He was sure he saw a Notfer and a Fumer hand in hand. The terror on their faces made them look like a brother and a sister.

Then Ben caught sight of Volka's red mane of hair flashing through the trees. He saw her disappear through a gap in a withered hedge. 'Rusalka! There's Volka! Down there! Put me down, I'll follow her.'

Rusalka could do nothing but watch as Ben ran along paths and through gaps too small for her. Eventually Ben came to a tiny, tumbledown wooden hut. 'Let me in!' He hammered on the door. 'Volka, Rusalka needs you, urgently. Come on!'

Slowly the door creaked open. Bending down to get in, Ben looked into the gloomy little room. He gasped. He hadn't for a moment expected this. 'You're *all* here! Rusalka's been calling you. She needs you.'

Staring back at Ben were all four keepers, sitting huddled in a circle on the floor. Vigil's small head whizzed round a few times. 'She can't possibly want us to help, we're the ones who failed her. She's only calling us so she can punish us.'

Terpia's waterfall hair was dripping onto the floor, along with the sea-blue tears streaming from her eyes. 'We've decided it's best for everyone if we sit here and await our deaths. If Rusalka can save the forest and its people, all well and good, but we don't deserve to be saved. We deserve to die.' With that her whole face dissolved into crying.

'But no, you idiots!' Ben knew this was rude, but time was short and he hurried on. 'It's *you* we need. We can't put the Spectrum back together without you. You must come.'

The ground was vibrating from Timor's shaking. Even his voice was wobbly. 'But Rusalka will be angry with us. We're in for big trouble if we see her.'

Ben flung open the hut door so they could see the devastation outside: the fallen trees, the fires, the dead flowers and animals. 'Timor, do you really think you could be in any more trouble than you're in now? Stop thinking of yourselves all the time. Hasn't it occurred to you that Rusalka feels guilty too? It was she who left you alone for so long. She could have run away and never come back for fear of getting into trouble herself with the Wisdom Speaker.'

When he said this, all four little bodies jerked upright. 'The Wisdom Speaker!' They all said together.

'Rusalka has dared to speak to the Wisdom Speaker about the forest?' said an astonished-looking Vigil, his head spinning round and round.

'Of course she has. She spoke to him as soon as she knew what was happening. She would do anything to save the forest. And so would I. I love it.'

All four faces gazed up into his. They saw a very dirty human child, with mud all over him, his black hair covered in dust, a line of blood on his cheek where a branch had caught him, and tears drawing wiggly lines down his muddy face. 'It might be too late, the forest might have died. But if there's just a tiny chance, just one in a billion, that *you* can save it, don't you want to try? How could you not want to try?'

They stared at Ben and said nothing. That's it, he thought, I've failed. They won't come. He looked at them one last time and left the hut, stumbling back in the direction he had left Rusalka as quickly as he could. 'Hang on, Ben! Wait a minute, our legs are shorter than yours!'

He turned to see all four keepers running as fast as they could towards him. 'Yes!' Ben laughed and shouted all at once.

Rusalka saw them coming and clapped her hands in excitement. She gathered Ben and the keepers in her arms and kissed them gently on their cheeks. It was difficult to carry all five of them but nobody minded being squashed, and in seconds they were all at the golden table in the centre of the forest.

Now that she had the keepers and Ben together, Rusalka seemed to know exactly what to do. Ben wondered if it was the Wisdom Speaker's wisdom she had drunk earlier. 'Ben, you stand in the middle. The rest of you, form a circle round him. Ben, give each one their piece of the Spectrum back.'

'Give it back!' said Ben. 'But I worked so hard to get them to give their pieces to me. I needn't have bothered.'

Rusalka talked quickly because she was in a hurry, but she had a half-smile on her face when she said to Ben, 'It was important they gave up their piece to you. It showed they were willing for things to change, but now it is important that together they put back what they broke. Come on, Ben. Stand in the centre with the pieces.'

So Ben got out the pieces from the purse around his neck for the last time. He held them in his cupped hands. Together, Volka, Timor, Vigil and Terpia stood round him and reached out for their piece. Everything, even the crashing and falling of the forest, seemed to grow silent, as if the forest was holding its breath. 'Now!' Rusalka whispered, 'Put them together. Put them together on Ben's hands.'

It wasn't at all clear to Ben how they were going to do that. They weren't shapes that naturally went together. How do you join a jagged lightning bolt to a teardrop? But Ben kept quiet. All four keepers placed their pieces in his hands at precisely the same time. As the pieces of crystal landed in his palms, he suddenly knew something he hadn't known before. The tears he had drunk from the bottom of the bowl were at work in him too, though he hadn't realised it. It was more than glass he held in his hand. He held the hearts of the keepers themselves. He felt their four personalities coming together, and he watched, fascinated, as the crystal grew hot and melted on his palms. Vigil, Volka, Terpia and Timor joined hands in the circle. The thick liquid moved in his hand, rolling and twisting. It's happening, he thought. It's worked. A feeling of joy filled Ben's body and bolted down his arms so hard it

would have hurt if it hadn't been so wonderful. His hands burned with happiness, and then it surged out of his fingertips in shots of colour. The colour flowed into the crystal sphere that had taken shape on his palms. Colours he had never seen in his life before darted around inside the crystal and it hummed and buzzed with a most beautiful sound.

Ben looked up and saw that Rusalka and the keepers now had their backs to him, looking into the forest, and immediately he knew why. Putting the Spectrum on the table, he went and stood next to them.

All around them, trees were straightening up, pulling their long trunks off the ground and reaching up their boughs to the sky as if they were stretching after a long sleep. As Rusalka, the keepers and Ben watched, the bark grew dry and firm, bare branches sprang buds, and hundreds of tiny new leaves appeared and unfurled. The rotten flowers, whose colour had dripped off their petals and fallen into the mud, stood back up straight again, their colour restored. The air filled with twittering and branches stretched themselves out, strong and firm, to support dozens of chirruping birds. And for the first time during the whole of this strange adventure, Ben took a deep breath through his nose. It smelt wonderful. The forest floor was no longer muddy and slippery, but soft and springy, lined with beautiful perfumed flowers and sweet-smelling shrubs that swayed and moved as if they were waving.

None of them could speak. They were happy and relieved and proud, all at once. More and more forest people started to crawl out from their hiding places. Ben had never seen joy like it. Unable at first to believe it was true, they stood staring and breathing in deeply through their noses. Then one little voice let out a whoop and then another and another, and within seconds, there were hundreds and hundreds of Notfers, Sobalots, Fumers and Trembolos. They danced and jumped, laughed and hugged. The forest grew thicker and greener by the second as they celebrated.

A Trembolo came and danced close to Ben, bouncing high off the ground with her wing-like arms. She noticed the Spectrum on the golden table. 'The Spectrum! It's whole again!'

The words bounced through the crowd, from one mouth to another. They all stood still and the silence passed like a ripple through the throng of little bodies. Then gradually, slowly, they all came and stood in front of it. The Spectrum glowed brightly and sang out a perfect pure note. They all smiled, and Ben realised that this wasn't a new sound for them, as it was for him. They were remembering how it used to be.

Rusalka took to the air and hovered over them all, swathes of colour wrapping round her and painting the air with every move she made. She lifted her arms and held them in the air for a few seconds. Everyone watched, and Ben could tell they all knew she was about to do something impressive. Slowly she floated her arms down. As she did, hovering next to her in the air, there appeared an enormous banqueting table laid with the most bright and colourful-looking food. The forest people cheered and jumped up and down in delight, scampering out of the way so that the feast could float down to the floor, more like a feather than a heavy wooden table.

Rusalka raised her graceful arms and there was silence once more. 'Let us eat, my friends, to celebrate the wholeness of the Spectrum, and the health of the forest – your home for as long as you look after it. The Spectrum is back together again and so are you. Learn from your mistakes, as I have from mine. Live together, all of you: Fumers, Trembolos, Notfers and Sobalots. Love one another and learn from one another. And I promise I will never stay away for too long again.' Here Rusalka paused and looked at Ben with a smile. Ben felt he was being washed in sunshine.

'And one more thing, before we eat and celebrate. We all have to thank our human child. Without his help, the Spectrum and the forest could not have been saved. Ben's human nature, that can understand and know the feelings of *all* our tribes, was the glue that stuck our Spectrum back together again.'

Ben felt hundreds of sets of eyes fixed on him. He didn't know what to do or say. Rusalka swooped over to him and picked him up into her hand. 'Ben, our human child, thank you.' A cheer far louder than Ben would have thought possible from such little mouths went up. Rusalka flew around the gathering with Ben as they waved and cheered. The pointed ears of a Notfer, the blue and white striped face of a Sobalot, two round Fumer nostrils and the pure white of a Trembolo's hair – all swam in and out of view as Rusalka flew him round the circle for his lap of honour. Faster and faster she flew until all he could see was a blur and all he could hear was a roar of voices. He felt the colours of Rusalka wrap round and round him until he couldn't see anything but bright light and then blackness.

He sat up, panting. He was in his tree house, alone. He heard the whine of the lawn mower outside; he smelt the freshly cut grass. Rays of golden light were flooding in through the gaps in the wood. It was a sunny day. He didn't move for a minute. He wanted to go back. He wanted to be in the forest.

'Ben! Ben, where are you?'

It was Anna.

'What?' he shouted back. He heard how unfriendly his voice sounded.

'Mum says we have to tidy our room before tea. We've got half an hour.' Anna called to him from below. She was never allowed inside the tree house.

Ben realised he was very, very hungry. So hungry he didn't even ask what was for tea. He would happily eat anything. He looked out of the doorway of his tree house and saw Anna was already going through the back door to the house. He followed, wishing she knew that her big brother had just saved hundreds of lives. That would make her treat him with a bit more respect.

He trudged up the stairs after her and stood in the doorway of their bedroom. Anna was plucking her toys off the floor and throwing them into a big blue storage box. Ben's eyes automatically looked to the plug socket behind the computer. The plug was still lying on the carpet. 'You can't play on the computer for the rest of the day, Mum says, so don't bother turning it on. If you do, I'll just unplug it again.'

Ben stepped into the room and felt anger bubbling inside him. He felt the heat rising in his body and his fists clenched. From nowhere, a picture of Volka came into his head. He saw her stamping her big feet, he saw her puffing steam out of her huge nostrils. He was so pleased to see Volka, he almost forgot he was angry and wanted to laugh.

He breathed out heavily through his nose, imagining his nostrils big and steamy, and he stamped his foot so hard that the plug next to his foot bounced off the floor. Anna looked scared. 'Anna,' said Ben, his voice serious but calm, 'I want you to know that I hated it when you pulled the plug out of my computer. It made me feel you don't care about what is important to me. I would really like it if you never pulled the plug out when I'm playing on the computer.'

Anna looked up at him, a beanie baby dangling from her left hand. Ben had never spoken to her like this before. She was startled. 'I'm sorry, Ben. I don't like it when you play on it for a long time, because it means you don't play with me. And then you go off to your tree house and I've got no one.'

Ben sat down on the carpet opposite her. 'Sometimes I need to be on my own, Anna. But I'll try and play with you more. Tell you what, if you don't pull the plug out all week, I'll let you play in the tree house with me – just for a bit.'

Anna smiled the smile she usually kept for her birthday morning. She ran downstairs to tell her mum what Ben had said. He stayed where he was. In a way he couldn't quite understand, he was certain that, for the rest of his life, he would remember the keepers.

And he was right. He would think about them when he couldn't sleep at night, he would think about them in his tree house (which never was taken down) and at school, and much later he would think of them when he was grown up and married, with his own children. But the moments when he remembered them most clearly, so clearly it was as if they were standing next to him, would be when he was very afraid, very angry, very jealous or very sad. At those times, it was as if he had friends standing right next to him who knew exactly how he felt and whose strange colourful bodies steamed, or spun, or stamped, or shook or cried along with him. And Ben knew that whatever happened to him, he had been a very lucky human child.

Overall aim To give closure to the piece of work, to emphasise that a full range of emotions are valuable and that by getting to know them we can make life better for ourselves and others.

ROUND 1

Aim To warm up, make contact, have fun.

Sitting game Divide the class into two equal groups. Each group stands in a circle. The children turn to the left so that they are facing the back of the child in front – still in a circle. Ask the children to shuffle together so that they are touching the person in front. On the count of 3 everyone gently sits on the knees of the person behind. When this is done properly, every child is supported and the circle is transformed into a human seat. This may take practice. It is a lot of fun.

ROUND 2

Aim To have fun and mix up the children.

All change The teacher instructs the children to exchange places with others, as follows:

- ◆ *Change places everyone with blue eyes.*
- ◆ *Change places everyone wearing red.*
- ◆ *Change places everyone who is grumpy in the morning.*
- ◆ *Change places everyone who likes chocolate.*

ROUND 3

Aim To engage with the story, to reflect on the feelings aroused by it, to encourage self-awareness, and to learn about feelings and empathy.

Question What is your favourite part of Chapter 6?

Question Were there any times in the chapter when you felt any emotions? (Were you worried, frustrated, sad, happy, confused?)

Try to give each child the opportunity to answer both questions.

It is important that each child's emotional disclosure is met with an empathic response. This can be made by one of the children. If it isn't, you need to acknowledge and receive the feeling. (See teacher's notes on page vii). This models to the children how to respond to feelings.

ROUND 4

Aim To learn about feelings and empathy.

Discussion Talk about Ben and how he saved the forest.

The idea is to pull out some key points from the discussion: specifically that we humans are able to experience the rich world of feeling and that it is valuable to us. The Notfers, Fumers, Sobalots and Trembolos are only able to experience one feeling. Ben makes friends with the feelings (keepers) through getting to know them (empathy). The children can learn to befriend their feelings and the feelings of others, making life better for themselves and those around them. When Ben has met and made friends with all the tribes the forest is restored, everyone celebrates and is very happy.

ROUND 5

Aim To move towards closure.

Open forum to hear any further thoughts or last words.

Ask if anyone would like to say or ask anything about Ben, Rusalka and the forest, or feelings.

If prompts are needed, you can ask the children about their favourite/most exciting/saddest/funniest part of the whole story.

ROUND 6

Aim To close.

Pass a smile All stand in a circle holding hands. Pass a smile round the circle, starting with the teacher and the child on their right. When that child sees the smile, they smile at the child on their right and so on. Once the first smile is on its way, the teacher sends a second smile round in the opposite direction by smiling at the child on their left.

CREATIVE ACTIVITY 1

Tastes and smells

This activity promotes reflection on the senses in a way that the children will enjoy. You will need a variety of foods of different flavours, including some salty (crisps, anchovies, olives), sweet (sweets, honey, banana), sour (lemon, lime, vinegar) and bitter (coffee, lemon pith).

The children are invited to taste the foods and discuss the flavours. Ask which ones they like/dislike. Do they have any associations between flavours and feelings, flavours and colours, flavours and sounds, flavours and textures? There are no right answers here; all are valid and all are interesting.

This activity lends itself to numeracy work in terms of charting preferences.

CREATIVE ACTIVITY 2

Collage

You will need fabric, a large roll of paper, sequins, feathers, ribbons, pom poms, glitter, glue, scissors.

Make a class collage of the forest celebration as a communal act to end the story.

CREATIVE ACTIVITY 3

Group sculpture

Divide the children into five groups of roughly equal size. Each group works with a different cameo from the chapter. We suggest you use the following:

- ◆ *The keepers in the hut.*
- ◆ *Rusalka and Ben with the Wisdom Speaker.*
- ◆ *Ben and the keepers restoring the Spectrum.*
- ◆ *Rusalka conjuring the banquet.*
- ◆ *Ben, Rusalka and the keepers flying.*

The groups choose or are allocated a scene, and then everyone decides which part they are going to play. They can be a tree or a seat or another inanimate object if they want. Give the groups time to rehearse their piece. The task is to create a tableau or a sculpture of the scene for the other children to see. When they are ready to show their piece every group performs in turn to the others. You can give each group a count of 10 as they move into position, arriving at the final sculpture on 10. Ask them to hold their position for a couple of minutes so the whole class can see. The groups are applauded after every piece. The children will catch on quickly and engage with the story.

As an extension to this you can ask the children how they feel when holding their position in the sculpture.

CREATIVE ACTIVITY 4

Dramatic musical extravaganza

You will need a wide variety of instruments, preferably all the ones used in the previous activities, and space for all the children to move about. If you have been making masks and puppets, you can use these too. This activity can be accompanied by reading the passage starting *All around them trees were straightening up* on page 74 to *Rusalka raised her graceful arms and there was silence once more* on page 75. Start by inviting the children to explore the instruments and notice what each sounds like. Allow a few minutes for this. If you have included music and dance as a regular part of the activities they will be familiar with the form. Each child then chooses an instrument to play. As with previous music activities, you may prefer to do this activity in small groups.

Each child can choose to be a character from the forest and wear an appropriate mask or hold the appropriate puppet. You might like to have half playing the instruments and half dancing, then get them to swap over. Encourage the children to use all the space in the room. Drawing a picture (or some lines) on the floor in chalk for them to dance over will help.

As usual noise is fine. Bring the extravaganza to a close, either by joining in and beginning to conduct, then with exaggerated body movements and arm waving lower the volume and bring the music to silence; or by playing some quiet music. You might like to take the opportunity to have a party to celebrate the restoration of the forest. Traditional party games like musical bumps will add to the fun.

The tribe of happy feelings

glad

joy

contentment

happy

satisfaction

pleasure

bliss

thrilled

amusement

delight

relief

ecstasy

Permission to Photocopy

Permission to Photocopy

BIBLIOGRAPHY

Goleman, D. (1996)
Emotional Intelligence.
London: Bloomsbury

Landreth, G. (2002)
Play Therapy.
New York: Brunner-Routledge

Mosley, J. (1993)
Turn Your School Round.
Cambridge: LDA

McLaughlin, C., Clark, P. and Chisholm, M. (1996)
Counselling and Guidance in Schools.
London: David Fulton Publishers

Salzberger-Wittenberg, I., Henry, G. and Osborne, E. (1999)
The Emotional Experience of Learning and Teaching.
London: Karnac Books

USEFUL WEBSITES

www.antidote.org.uk

www.childmentalhealthcentre.org

www.bacp.co.uk

www.psychotherapy.org

FURTHER READING

Axline, V. (2001)
*Dibs: In Search of Self: Personality Development
in Play Therapy.*
London: Ballantine

Daniels, D. and Jenkins, P. (2000)
*Therapy with Children: Children's Rights, Confidentiality
and the Law.*
London: Sage

Mearns, D. and Thorne, B. (1999)
Person-centred Counselling in Action.
London: Sage

Miller, A. (1995)
*The Drama of Being a Child and the Search
for the True Self.*
London: Virago

Oaklander, V. (1981)
Windows to our Children.
Moab, Utah: Real People Press

Stern, D. (2000)
The Interpersonal World of the Infant.
London: Basic Books

Sunderland, M. (2000)
Stories for Troubled Children.
Oxford: Speechmark

Sunderland, M. (2000)
Using Story Telling as a Therapeutic Tool with Children.
Oxford: Speechmark

Whitehouse, E. and Pudney, W. (1997)
A Volcano in my Tummy – Helping Children to Handle Anger.
Gabriola Island: New Society Publishers